BEFORE THE
FIRST DAY

Leander R Pimenta

The full story of the Earth's Creation

'In the beginning God created the heavens and the Earth'
(Genesis 1:1)

*'What really interests me is whether God had any choice
in the creation of the world'*
(Albert Einstein)

BEFORE THE FIRST DAY
Leander R Pimenta

Published by:
Creation Books
PO Box 17, Chichester, West Sussex, PO20 6YB, England

Distributed by:
New Wine Ministries
22 Arun Business Park, Bognor Regis, West Sussex, PO22 9SX, England

ISBN 1-874367-83-3
First printing January 1998
Second printing October 1998

Design, artwork and illustrations by:
Jacamar, 8 The Green, Rowlands Castle, Hampshire

Printed in England by:
Clays Ltd, St Ives plc.

BEFORE THE
FIRST DAY

ERRATA

In this printing some words on the last line on a few pages may be faint or missing and the author and publisher offers their sincerest apologies for this production error which has occured for reasons beyond their control. The pages which may be affected are as follows:

Page	Missing or faint words on last line:
32	gravity to
117	implications
131	the Bible seriously
132	Comets orbit the sun with periods varying from less than a
133	may divert any giant asteroid away from us. We saw one
157	to worry about
206	is composed of eight protons and eight to ten neutrons in the
211	as
230	themselves orbiting in the fog of the dense and heavier
240	System

For Paul, Dominic and Rebecca

BEFORE THE FIRST DAY

CONTENTS

PREFACE

During only the last few thousand years, the Earth has been subjected to ten stupendous global events which have had a profound effect on the physical features of our planet. The widespread ignorance about these events is quite astonishing and their cause, importance and effects have never before received the attention they deserve. This book gives a logical account of these events which may be listed as follows:

1 The Earth becomes a dark watery planet with no dry land. The Sun remains a darkened star.

2 A small planet about half the size of the Moon 'soft' lands on the Earth and breaks up.

3 An extremely massive planet, larger than Jupiter, comes in close proximity to the Earth.

4 The Earth loses billions of tonnes of ocean water and air which is sucked out into space.

5 The ocean bed throughout the Earth is raised and cracked open causing deep fissures that stretch for thousands of kilometres.

6 A near circular submerged supercontinent is raised above sea level and becomes dry land.

7 The Moon is pulled out of its independent orbit and falls into the Earth's captivity.

8 A rise in the bed of the Pacific Ocean causes the supercontinent to become completely submerged again.

9 A sudden deepening of the Pacific Ocean allows the supercontinent to become dry land once more.

10 The supercontinent breaks up into continents which drift apart for thousands of kilometres.

1

These events are truly startling and of such a magnitude that most people would find it hard to believe that they ever happened.

While some Earth scientists may be prepared to acknowledge that some of these events could possibly have taken place hundreds of millions of years ago, any suggestion that they happened only within the last few thousand years would not be well received. This, they would say, is not in accordance with the many current and popular theories used by scientists to explain the origin of the Earth.

We know that these events did occur during only the last few thousand years for two reasons.

Firstly, some of the evidence of their effects is still fresh on the Earth today. This only becomes clear once the events are understood.

Secondly, the Bible tells us either directly or by inference that these major events did occur. For many people this is a good enough reason because there is no scientific evidence to disprove any biblical truths.

That there is widespread ignorance and disbelief about these events can be attributed to two very different attitudes.

Firstly, many scientists simply do not wish to believe that such global catastrophes could have affected our planet so recently.

This is mainly because these scientists have put their faith in the theory of uniformitarianism which postulates that the Earth is billions of years old and that our planet has been in a comparatively tranquil state for most of this time. Slow evolutionary processes, they say, have continued without interruption for all these thousands of millions of years and all the physical features of the Earth can, they say, be explained in terms of very gradual changes. There is therefore no room to accommodate any of the catastrophic events mentioned above within the framework of uniformitarianism theories. And so even the worldwide Deluge which killed millions of people only about 4400 years ago is not acknowledged by many Earth scientists.

Secondly, people who can accept biblical truths have not in general been too willing or able to explain the truths regarding our planet in scientific terms. This is often due to the mistaken belief that there is no scientific explanation for what they believe to be supernatural acts of God.

Hence the real reason why so little is known of these stupendous events is that hitherto there has been no one to write about and explain these events.

The problem is further compounded because neither Earth scientists nor Bible believers have a very clear idea of how our planet was designed and constructed. Because of this, the possibility of major upheavals of the kind listed above have not been thought possible and therefore not given the consideration they deserve.

Two more global events are predicted by the Bible for the very near future. The first will involve another close encounter with a massive swarm of comets resulting in a bombardment of the Earth by giant asteroids and meteorites. The second will involve the Sun whose behaviour will become highly erratic and result in the Sun becoming unbearably hot. Everything on the Earth will finally be dried up and scorched.

If we are to understand the catastrophic events that have already taken place and the catastrophes still to come we need a very clear idea about how the entire Solar System (and especially the Earth) was formed in the first place. Thus the reasons for writing this book are twofold.

Firstly, it is to give a logical, step by step, account of how the Earth was created from the nothingness of cold dark and empty space.

Secondly, it is to describe the cause, effects and significance of all twelve global events outlined above.

The story of the creation the Earth and the subsequent global events that have befallen it are closely related. Both can be explained by just ONE quite simple scientific theory.

Very briefly, this simple theory postulates that our Sun was once a double or binary star which subsequently collapsed into a single star. The entire Solar System is the remnant of that collapse. The laws of nature, as we understand them, and well established facts about our Universe and planet discovered over the centuries by workers in all disciplines, but specially in Astronomy and Geology, are almost all we need to explain our planet.

We say almost, because it is easy to forget that everything that has ever been built in a thoughtful manner must have started with a designer. The Earth is no exception to this rule.

Some would say that 'Nature' is the designer and constructor of the Earth and this would not be totally incorrect because 'Nature' is the physical manifestation of God's creative Spirit in action. So ultimately it is God and not 'Nature' who is the designer and creator of the entire Universe.

However the words 'God' and 'Nature' are interchangeable in this book. The word 'Nature' will be used widely in this book as it is felt that most readers may feel more comfortable with this term. It has also made the writing of this book a little easier. The reader is of course free to substitute the word 'God' for 'Nature' if preferred and there should be no loss of meaning if this is done.

This book thus describes a theory about how 'Nature' went about the task of creating the Earth. It is a scientific theory in that it is based on much that science has told us and the laws of nature as we understand them. This theory offers an acceptable explanation for all the features of the Earth and the rest of the Solar System. To the best of the author's knowledge no other single theory, as powerful as the one postulated in this book, has been published.

What makes this particular theory for explaining the formation of our planet quite unique is that it is also supported by a large number of verses in the Bible. The Bible makes several references to aerial and terrestrial phenomena and, if these references are taken as being correctly reported, we have an invaluable insight into how our universe began and how the Earth was created. It is an insight that we can hardly ignore. The Biblical references fit in well with the binary sun theory, so it may be said that this book presents a new story of the Earth's creation that is based on *discovered* scientific truths but also confirmed and reinforced by *revealed* Biblical truths.

Finally in this Preface I ought to present my credentials for publishing a book of this kind.

Firstly, I am a Bible believing Christian. I believe that the Bible is the inspired Word of God and everything that it contains is true. The Bible has much to say about past and present human existence on this planet and the eternal life to come. In this respect the Earth is just a temporary place for humans to live out their lives and learn how to survive for eternity.

Secondly, I hold two university degrees in related subjects. I have thus been able to study existing theories about our planet and am aware of their very serious shortcomings.

Thirdly, I have specialised in Geotechnical engineering to earn my living. This has enabled me to look at soil and rock formations at hundreds of locations on four continents so I can comment with some authority on the stuff from which our planet is made.

Fourthly, as a university lecturer and Civil engineer my job is to explain the science of construction. I see the Earth as one big construction project that involves an architect (God or Nature), the gathering together of the necessary materials in the right amounts and at the right time, and the orderly assembly of these materials. Having obtained a clear picture about this I wish to share it with anyone who may have also have become dissatisfied with current theories.

Fifthly, this is the second edition of this book. The first edition was produced for the sole reason of eliciting comments from professional people in all disciplines from all over the world. In particular reviewers were asked to look out for any scientific or scriptural inaccuracies. As a result of their comments this edition has been revised and rearranged.

Finally, this book is the culmination of almost fifteen years of contemplation of a subject that had to make sense to me from a professional as well as a spiritual view point. I am naturally excited by what I have discovered and I wish to share this excitement.

This book contains ten chapters and ten appendices. The ten chapters tell the whole story but readers wishing to have a little more detail may go on to study the appendices. I will be grateful to receive comments and questions.

Leander R Pimenta
26 PO10 7LT
Emsworth, Hampshire, England
e-mail: LRP@newnet.co.uk

CHAPTER ONE

TRUTH AND THEORY

Biblical truth or secular theories?

'With my great power...I made the Earth (Jer.27:5)

The biblical truth is that the Earth was created by God.

This truth is still widely accepted by the vast majority of people in the world today but there is undoubtedly a growing number of people who cannot accept this truth and prefer to believe that the Earth was not deliberately made but evolved by natural processes without any input from a Creator.

Today the biblical truth is challenged by various theories proposed by scientists. These theories have gained some acceptance and are almost regarded as the truth by the media and our educational institutions.

To set the background to this book it is necessary to take a brief look at these theories.

The first theory deals with the very start of the Universe. This is popularly known as the Big Bang theory which speculates that the Universe began some ten to fifteen billion years ago in a gigantic burst of radiation and expansion of space. This event, the theory postulates, eventually resulted in the formation of a huge expanding sphere of hydrogen and helium gas.

A second theory takes over at this stage to explain how this immense sphere of hydrogen and helium became fragmented and compressed to form stars and galaxies of stars.

A third theory is then used to explain how stars change during their life time and how the hydrogen they contain becomes 'cooked' into other elements before exploding as a supernova.

A fourth theory with many different variations explains why some stars subsequently develop planetary systems like ours. Dozens of different theories for the Solar System have been proposed throughout the ages but none have been found to be entirely satisfactory. The problem has been found to be so difficult that many scientists believe that a simple theory for the formation of the Solar System that is capable of explaining all its features has not been found and probably does not exist.

Our planet is layered with very different types of material in each layer. At the Earth's centre is a core believed to be made from iron. Covering this core is at least seven further layers of material the topmost one being the atmosphere. There are theories for the origin, composition and thickness of each of these layers.

Our planet now has a unique atmosphere of oxygen and nitrogen but secular theories suggest that it once had an atmosphere of hydrogen. Other theories suggest that the early atmosphere was methane and carbon dioxide. There are thus more theories on how the Earth's atmosphere changed from its past one to its present one.

The vast quantity of water in the Earth's oceans is also something of a mystery. There are theories about how the oceans were formed. Some scientists say that all the water came from volcanoes. Other scientists think much of the water came from comets that crashed on to the Earth.

The existence of continents of dry land on this planet is also a problem. If all the water in the Earth today was evenly distributed throughout the globe then we would hardly have any dry land but just a few scattered tiny islands in one global ocean several thousand metres deep.

But the fact is that a third of the Earth's surface is land and most of this land is on one side of the globe only. The problem of the formation of the Earth's continents has not hitherto been solved although several theories for it have been proposed.

We now know that all the continents were once joined together in one huge near circular supercontinent. Just why this super-continent had to be near circular has hitherto not been explained.

This supercontinent has now broken up and there are further theories for how and when the continents drifted apart.

Our planet is blessed with a huge variety of soils, rocks and minerals and coal and oil deposits. More theories to explain all these have been proposed.

Our planet has an amazing biosphere with countless millions of species of land and marine life. Several theories that try to explain the origin of life have been proposed.

Our planet has been subject to catastrophes on a global scale from time to time and for this reason we have a good fossil record showing periodic mass extinctions of all forms of life. Several theories as to the cause and timing of these catastrophes have been suggested. The theory of asteroids hitting the Earth has grown in popularity in recent years.

The Earth has a magnetic field which is rapidly decreasing in strength and should disappear altogether in a few thousand years. The origin of the Earth's magnetic field and its decreasing strength is also subject for more theories.

The Moon is our nearest neighbour and is so large that the Earth/Moon system is regarded as a double or binary planet. We know a great deal about the Moon but there is still (until now) no fully acceptable theory as to how it might have formed. One such theory, recently proposed, postulates that the Moon was pushed out of the Earth as a result of a collision between the Earth and another small planet. This theory explains very little and, as we will see, is cumbersome and incorrect.

Our Sun is another problem. Although it is the nearest star to us we still do not know enough about it. We are not entirely sure about its source of heat or why it oscillates or why its rate of heat production is so uniform. The popular theory is that the heat is produced by thermonuclear reactions deep in its interior. This theory does not explain everything. Our Sun suffers from periodic blemishes on its face in the form of sunspots. These spots have worried people for centuries and continues to intrigue scientists even today and theories for their existence and behaviour have been proposed. The predictable appearance of spots is not compatible with the idea of thermonuclear reactions and extremely high temperatures.

From this brief scenario it is evident that to gain a 'scientific' understanding of how our Earth was formed it is necessary to evaluate very many theories proposed at different times by different people.

It is not relevant to discuss the merits and shortcomings of each of these many theories here but it is not difficult to find problems with most of the theories mentioned above. Most importantly the various theories are not always compatible with each other and are not supported by scripture. From all the various theories that scientists have proposed so far it cannot be concluded with any confidence that we have a clear picture of how the Earth was formed.

Science has made us consider different theories and this is good because science progresses in this way. But it is easy to get over enthusiastic about a particular theory and assume it to be the truth. This is a common mistake that scientists frequently make. We can safely conclude that existing secular scientific theories have not disproved the biblical truth that the Earth was made by God and it is quite wrong to think that science has disproved any biblical truth.

A scientific theory compatible with biblical truth

Biblical truths on their own cannot be used to challenge any of the theories that are used by secular scientists to explain our planet. Secular scientists do not accept the authority of the Bible and are unlikely to be persuaded by scripture.

10

To challenge secular theories, Bible believers need true facts as well as a plausible theory. The facts have to be scientifically established and should be acceptable by all scientists whatever their opinion on the origin of the Earth might be. Any theory that is proposed by Bible believers must not only be scientifically plausible and superior to secular theories, but must also be in accordance with the scriptures. Such a theory is the theme of this book.

The starting point for this new theory must be the biblical truth that in the beginning God *created* the Earth. Now if we accept this truth from scripture, then we also have to accept that God made the Earth from materials that were already in existence. All the evidence points out to the fact that the process of construction must have been a natural one and the Earth looks as if it was formed perfectly naturally.

The scriptures also tell us that once the process of creation was completed, God had a look to see the results (presumably of the work of Nature) and was proud and pleased with what He saw. (Gen.1:31)

Hence in order to defend the biblical truth of creation from the attack by secular theories, it is necessary to have a clear picture of how natural forces were used and how these resulted in the creation of the Earth. This is what this book is all about.

It is convenient to consider the chain of events leading to the Earth's creation in two parts.

The first part, called 'the beginning' started at the very beginning of the Universe and ended at the stage when the Earth had grown to its present size and became completely engulfed in a deep ocean of water. All this happened in an unknown period of time *before the first day*.

The first day was when the Earth enjoyed its first evening and morning, and this was only about six thousand years ago.

The second part, called 'the making' began on this first day

11

and was completed in a period of less than a week. During this extremely brief period of time the dark watery planet was transformed naturally, yet dramatically, into a glorious planet with night and day and dry land.

Hence any scientific theory proposed for how the Earth was formed should also explain how and why our planet was once a dark watery planet and how and why it then became completely transformed in only a few days by perfectly natural forces into more or less what it is today. This is what is attempted in this book.

Very briefly this book proposes that the whole of the Solar System including the Earth was created as a consequence of the formation and subsequent collapse of a binary star.

An atom of hydrogen is a binary system with an electron in orbit round a proton. This is the starting point for our story of the Earth's creation. From a binary atom it is not difficult to show how rotating binary clouds of hydrogen were formed. From one such binary cloud our binary Sun was formed. And from the subsequent collapse of this binary Sun the planets were formed.

In this book we show that this theory, called the Binary Sun Theory, not only gives very satisfactory explanations for all the physical features of the Earth and other planets but also accounts for the following major global events which are mentioned in the Bible.

1. The formation of the 'foundations' of the Earth (Ps.104:5)
2. The formation of the Earths' oceans. (Job 38:8)
3. The existence of the Earth as a dark water covered planet in orbit round a dark Sun (Gen.1:2)
4. The dramatic formation of a submerged supercontinent (Ps.24:2)

5. The appearance of a very large and bright light powerful enough to light up half the Earth's surface (Gen.1.3)

6. The dramatic removal of a vast quantity of water from the Earth's global ocean (Gen.1:6)

7. The sudden appearance of a supercontinent of dry land (Gen.1:9)

8. The lighting up of the Sun just six thousand years ago (Gen 1:14)

9. The Global Flood that left no dry land anywhere on the Earth and lasted a year killing almost the entire population of the Earth about 4400 years ago.(Gen.7:11)

10. The splitting apart of the supercontinent about 4280 years ago. (Gen.10:25)

11. The erratic behaviour of our Sun (Is.30:26)

12. The predicted bombardment of the Earth by giant meteorites and asteroids during the end times.(Rev.8:8)

In the pages that follow the Binary Sun Theory for the formation of the Universe of galaxies and of the Solar System and of the Earth is developed.

If the theory is correct it means that the Earth did form quite naturally according to the laws of nature.

The theory that we propose is scientific in that no scientific laws or facts are ignored. But this does not diminish the simple truth that in the beginning God made the Earth because although we say Nature allowed the Earth to come into existence, it must be remembered that Nature is only a manifestation of the power and intelligence of the Spirit of God.

It is important to stress that what is proposed in this book is still only a theory. It is backed both by scriptures as well as science but it remains a theory.

Nature may have created the Earth and the Universe in a totally different way and we must retain an open mind on this issue.

Six days or six aeons?

'For in six days the Lord made heaven and earth, the sea and all that in them is...(Ex.20:11)

According to the theory described in this book, the Earth was constructed layer by layer and probably took only a few tens of thousands of years to complete. We do not know precisely when the construction process started and we do not know precisely when it was completed. However if we measure the age of the Earth from its first proper day and night then the Earth is only about six thousand years old. This can be worked out from the genealogies given in the Bible.

Before the first day the Earth was a dark planet completely engulfed in a global ocean of great depth. The Sun had not as yet begun to radiate heat and light. A dramatic event described later in this book resulted in a complete transformation of the Earth's surface and it is this transformation which took about six days. However many Bible believers wrongly think that the whole of planet Earth was created in six days.

This belief is not according to scripture. The word 'heaven' in the verse above does not refer to the Universe of galaxies but only to the space that was formed between two immense volumes of water. The first volume of water was the global ocean and the second volume of water was a huge canopy of water that was sucked up high above the surface of the Earth on the second day. The formation of this space between the waters is in accordance with the theory we propose and is explained later on in this book.

The word 'earth' in the above verse does not refer to the whole globe of the planet but only to the 'dry land' or supercontinent that emerged from under the oceans on the second day. Throughout the Bible the term 'earth' is used only for the continents and not for the whole globe. The sudden formation

14

of the first supercontinent can also be explained by the same theory.

The word 'sea' refers not to the global ocean but to the 'gathered waters' which indeed happened on the third day.

Before the first day the Earth was completely covered with water- the face of the deep that the Spirit of God was able to hover over.

Hence the belief by some Creationists that the Earth appeared in a fully formed state from nothing on the first day and is only six thousand years old is not scriptural and cannot be explained in scientific terms.

On the other extreme are secular scientists who believe that the Earth is some 4500 million years old. This is an unimaginably long period of time that does not really make much sense. We are told that life first appeared on this planet some five hundred million years ago and that the dinosaurs died out some sixty million years ago. We are also told that the continents began drifting apart some two hundred million years ago and man changed from apes to humans about a million years ago.

During all this seemingly infinite period of time the Earth is said to have cooled down from a once molten state. All the rocks and soils of the Earth are said to have been formed much later by weathering, erosion and deposition.

But according to the theory that is proposed in this book the Earth was built up layer by layer in very cold conditions. It was never in a hot molten state as secular scientists would have us believe. The Earth could never have been in a wholly molten state because had it been so its' rotation would have flattened it into a disc just like a ball of very soft clay on a rapidly rotating potters wheel soon flattens to a disc.

Our theory also suggests that the various soils and rocks found on the Earth were not formed in the way suggested by secular scientists but in a totally different way.

15

Catastrophic events such as the great Flood that completely engulfed all land masses on the Earth are regarded as pure myths by secular scientists.

Bible believers should realise that the idea of a 4500 million year old planet is neither scientific nor scriptural but is part of an elaborate deception. This deception has prevented many people from having a true understanding of the purpose of their very short lives on this planet.

According to the theory proposed in this book the Earth was built up fairly quickly over a period of at the most a few tens of thousands of years and was intended to last for only a few thousand years.

The Earth exists for one reason alone, and this is to provide an environment for man to prove himself as worthy enough to be trusted with the gift of eternal life. For those who pass the test, there are probably hundreds of far more suitable planets somewhere else in this vast Universe waiting to be inhabited in the fullness of time.

The prospect of eternal life is a wonderful hope to have but for some reason there are forces in the world today which are determined to prevent people from having this hope. The notion of a 4.5 billion year old planet that gives all the time that is required for atheistic evolution to take place is one of the deceptions that have been propagated with this in mind.

Further Reading
Levenson D A *Sense of the Earth* Doubleday & Co. New York 1972
Press F & Siever R *Earth* (Second Edition) W H Freeman & Co San Francisco 1977
Takeuchi, Uyeda & Kanamori *Debate About the Earth* Freeman Cooper & Co San Francisco 1970

CHAPTER TWO

SIGNS IN THE SKY

Asteroids as building bricks

'...and the stars in the sky fell to earth..' (Rev. 6:12)

Although the age of the Earth is often quoted as being some four or five billion years there are some clear indications in the skies that the Earth is so young that its construction is still going on today.

Each day thousands of tons of material from space, in the form of dust and meteorites, land on the Earth and quietly become part of this planet. Less frequently and thankfully, the Earth is subject to an impact from something much larger in the form of an asteroid of rock or ice, which results in a catastrophe of local or global proportions.

This continued addition of material (a process called accretion) to the Earth is an important and very relevant realisation and forms a good point to begin our story of the Earth's creation.

As recently as May 1996 Astronomers in the United States announced that they were surprised and somewhat perturbed to discover that there were so many (over 200) asteroids within the Solar System that were large enough to be detectable and trackable. Computations have shown that these would cross the path of the Earth's orbit in time but the chances of an actual collision between the Earth and one of these asteroids was considered to be slim. Many astronomers believe that the May 1996 estimate for such asteroids may be too low because asteroids are extremely difficult to detect until they come relatively close to the Sun, when they can reflect some of the light received from the Sun. But as our observation and computation techniques improve and more astronomers start to scrutineer photographs taken with the aid of powerful telescopes, the discovery of such asteroids is increasing rapidly, and at least one new such asteroid is found, named and catalogued every month. There is a growing fear that the chances of the Earth being hit by a sizeable asteroid is now so high that governments are being cautioned to make preparations for such an event and also to think of ways of detecting, diverting or destroying such asteroids whilst still out in space.

Our observational and computational skills have improved so much that once we have been able to firmly establish the path of an asteroid in the night sky, it becomes possible to determine if it will miss the Earth altogether or if it will be a close flyby or if it is on target to collide with the Earth. Refinements in these computations even make it possible to determine the time and place of an impending asteroid impact.

But there is nothing new about asteroid impacts. This has been going on ever since the Earth was just a ball of iron that began spiralling its way closer to the Sun from much further out in the Solar System than its present orbit.

The Earth was constructed, as we explain later, layer by layer as a result of billions of meteorite and asteroid impacts. Our planet (along with the others) may be crudely regarded as no more than a huge heap of crashed, disintegrated, melted and mangled asteroids, meteorites and dust from space.

But what makes this planet of ours not just a haphazard dumping ground for stray space debris but a preordained and deliberate work of creation is that all this material did not attach itself to the growing embryo of the Earth in a random way, but in an orderly yet perfectly natural way, as if Nature contrived it all, intending that the Earth and the other planets should become what they are today.

Indeed the presence of billions of fragments of debris, including thousands of large asteroids that float within the Solar System today in as many different orbits, is as much of a surprise as finding a few bricks on a building site around an almost completed building!

Thus to explain how the Earth was constructed we have to explain the origin of the hundreds of different types of dust, meteortites and asteroids from which the Earth was formed. And to do this properly we need to go right back in time to the very beginning of the Universe itself, when there were no clouds of gas or galaxies of stars. We do this in Appendix 1 and Appendix 2, but now it is helpful to take a brief look at some common features of the sky at night, because almost every object that can be observed gives us a little clue as to how the Earth was constructed.

The sky at night

'When I consider your heavens, the work of your fingers..'

(Ps. 8:3)

Astronomy is a branch of science that had its beginnings in almost all the ancient civilisations, but became more systematic during the last few centuries with the invention of the telescope. Today many households have a telescope or binoculars of some sort, and the heavens are open to inspection by anyone who cares to look.

Vast sums of money have been spent building bigger and better observatories with giant telescopes at locations through-

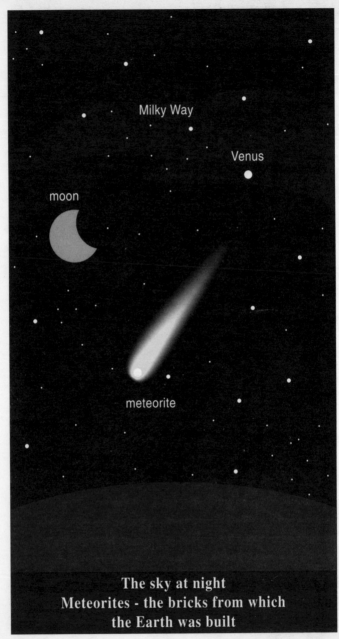

The sky at night
Meteorites - the bricks from which
the Earth was built

Fig. 2.1

out the world where clear skies can be expected for a good part of the year. These giant telescopes are in some ways a little outdated because we now have the technology to place telescopes out in space where problems of dust and light pollution do not arise. The Hubble Space Telescope regularly beams back to Earth crystal clear pictures of the stars, planets and distant galaxies and as a result of this magnificent achievement our knowledge of the Universe has greatly increased. In addition to optical telescopes we also have powerful radio telescopes, and radio astronomy has also helped us to understand a good deal more about our Universe.

But even with the naked eye or a good pair of binoculars there is much to see in the sky at night that is very relevant to our story of the Earth's creation and some of these objects may now be mentioned.

The planets

Among the brightest objects (after the Moon) seen in the sky at night would be one or more of the other planets of the Solar System, particularly Mars or Venus. There are only nine planets left in our Solar System at present, but we explain later why there were almost certainly many more of these earlier on.

All of the present planets revolve around the Sun in the same direction and in more or less the same plane. What this tells us is that our planet was not created in isolation but as part of a system with the other planets at about the same time by the same process. Hence to understand the beginning of the Earth we also need to understand the mechanism by which all the other planets came into existence. Later on in this book the formation of all the other planets is discussed in some detail.

The Moon

We can usually see the Moon in one of its phases even during the day and can observe it daily changing from a crescent to a full moon, depending on how it is able to reflect the Sun's light. Looking at the Moon we may wonder how it fits in with the creation of the Earth. Was it created at the same time or later on, we may well ask? We may also be inclined to think about the moons of other planets.

On closer study of these other moons we would discover that our planet is rather unique, in that it is the only planet with a moon that is relatively very large. The Earth and Moon are gravitationally bound to each other and the two bodies together may be regarded as a binary planet. In this book we have much to say about binary systems and their subsequent collapse, so we have on our doorstep an excellent example of a binary system.

The moons of other planets are comparatively much smaller than their parent planet. Our Moon is nearly a third of the size of the Earth. Our Moon was only recently captured by the Earth and later on in this book we explain how this came about.

It is often assumed that our Moon revolves around the Earth but this is not strictly true as both Earth and Moon behave as a binary planet and revolve around each other about a common centre of gravity. Because of the Earth's much greater mass the common centre of gravity in this case is not very far from the Earth's centre and so it appears that the Moon rotates about the Earth. The binary nature of the Earth/Moon is an important realisation, because the theme that we will use throughout this book is the formation and collapse of binary systems. A binary system of tiny particles started the universe as we explain in Appendix 2. We have binary galaxies in which a whole galaxy rotates about another galaxy. We also have numerous binary stars within our own galaxy and there is some evidence to suggest that within our own Solar System we once had binary planets not unlike the Earth/Moon binary. Our Sun once had a binary companion which subsequently became impacted into a single body, resulting as we shall see in the formation of all the planets of the Solar System. Hence the Earth/Moon binary affords an excellent opportunity for us to study and understand binary systems in general.

The stars

With a modest telescope or pair of binoculars we may on a perfectly dark night look further into the depths of space and see hundreds if not thousands of stars, some quite bright ones others very faint. We now have techniques for estimating the distance of each star from the Earth and if we used these we would soon realise that all stars are many thousands of billions of kilometres away. This would make us realise that the Solar System to which we belong occupies an almost insignificantly small part of the entire Universe.

We may quite rightly wonder if all these distant stars had anything to do with the creation of the Earth, as it would not appear to be the case. However, as we will learn later our Sun is just an ordinary star created in much the same way as all other stars and it is true to say that many of these distant stars did have a role, albeit tiny, to play in creating our planet, by virtue of their own mass and gravity, and this is also explained later.

The Milky Way

If conditions are right we may be fortunate enough to be able to discern a hazy band of faint light from millions of stars stretching from horizon to horizon. This spectacle is an insider's view of our own galaxy called the Milky Way galaxy and on a clear night we can see one of its spiral arms. Looking at this arm we may wonder if there is any significance in the fact that our galaxy has spiral arms and some other distant galaxies show no such arms. We explain later in this book that the existence of spiral arms is actually another clue to the formation of the Solar System and our planet Earth.

Comets

If we look really hard and use a telescope or pair of binoculars we may also perhaps pick up a comet or two, of which there are thousands currently in orbit round the Sun. A few times every century a large comet becomes visible with the naked eye and is often thought of as a bad omen. It is important to realise that a comet is simply a giant asteroid made mainly from volatile substances which 'evaporate' when the asteroid is hit by the stream of particles radiating from the Sun.

A comet in the night sky may be a beautiful sight to behold but it also tells us something extremely important about our own planet, and this is that our Solar System is not composed only of the Sun and its retinue of planets orbiting in one plane, but also of thousands if not millions of other giant asteroids in huge orbits at all angles to the plane of the Earth's orbit.

The possibility of collision between a comet and one of the planets is still very great indeed (for example the collision of Comet Shoemaker Levy and Jupiter recently) as there are so many comets sharing the same comparatively small volume of space around the Sun.

Most of the comets will eventually find their resting place on the Sun to which they are gravitationally bound and are gradually spiralling towards, but some comets have undoubtedly collided with other planets and become part of the planet and as we shall see, even a near miss of a massive comet and the Earth is sufficient to bring about great changes on the Earth's surface.

The presence of so many comets in the Solar System is another indication that the Solar System is young. The origin of comets is explained later in this book, and like asteroids we should not be surprised to find that there are so many of them still about.

A giant swarm of comets will play a major part in the devastation of this planet and this is described in the final chapter of this book.

Distant galaxies

If we were able to look past all the stars in our own galaxy with a powerful telescope we would discover that our Universe is not a random distribution of individual stars but is made up of huge concentrations of stars called galaxies. Between each galaxy is a vast amount of space with no visible stars at all. These galaxies are so far away that it is impossible to pick out individual stars in them, but if we could we would find that each galaxy was composed of billions of individual, binary and multiple system stars in all stages of development, just as the stars of our own galaxy. We would find some stars still barely formed and in a wholly gaseous state, others quite young and warm. We would see some blindingly hot and bright ones and sense the presence of very cold and dark and seemingly dead ones. We would also note that the distance between galaxies was vast and that the galaxies were not evenly distributed. We would note that some regions of the Universe have gigantic clusters of galaxies while other regions are completely void. We would learn that while many galaxies were moving away from each other, some galaxies were moving towards each other and on a collision course. We would also learn that some galaxies were in the process of a collision and other galaxies had just emerged from a collision with another galaxy.

We would note that although the galaxies were hurtling away and towards each other the individual galaxies themselves would seem to be tightening up and contracting rather than expanding.

Looking at these distant galaxies we would be tempted to wonder what our own galaxy looks like from afar. If somehow we could transport ourselves to near another cluster of galaxies and look back on our own from there we may be a little disappointed.

At first sight it would appear our galaxy was not very different from the millions of other galaxies. On a closer examination of it however, we would discover that it is shaped as a disc with a central bulge and untidy spiral arms, like a gigantic octopus lying flat on the sea bed with its arms loosely curled around it.

We may remark that the presence of these spiral arms does make our galaxy a little out of the ordinary after all.

From this distance we may even be able to pick out our Sun which we would see as just an ordinary star and one of the countless millions of other stars in our galaxy. We would note its position towards the edge of the galaxy and in one of the spiral arms.

We would be alarmed to discover that our galaxy was hurtling through space at a staggering six hundred kilometres per second.

We may then be tempted to compare our galaxy with other galaxies. We would note that although there are galaxies of all sizes there are not too many different shapes to choose from. We may ask if the shape of our galaxy has anything to do with the formation of the Earth. The answer, as we shall see later, is that it very probably has.

The Celestial Sphere

We cannot of course view our Universe from another galaxy and have to be content with viewing the Universe from a position inside our own galaxy.

Our view of the Universe is thus a little obstructed not only by the Earth's atmosphere and light pollution but also by immense clouds of gas/dust that are still present within our galaxy.

Despite these problems we must consider ourselves fortunate that we are we are able to study the Universe from the inside of our galaxy. This enables us to examine some of the individual stars in our galaxy that surround us on all sides. The more prominent and readily observable of these stars of our galaxy form a very convenient system of reference points, so that we can use them as markers and draw a map of the celestial sphere. This faithfully presents itself to us night after night throughout the year, and so with a well mapped out night sky, observations and studies of the objects in the Universe can be made and recorded in a systematic way, and astronomers are able to compare notes with each other. This has enabled us to build up a catalogue of stars within our own galaxy and to plot the location of other galaxies in the Universe relative to these stars.

Moving objects such as comets or individual asteroids within our own Solar system can also be tracked accurately using this reference system. These observations and studies together with the vastly increased power of our telescopes, has made us increasingly aware of the vast amount of debris still moving about within our Solar System.

We should watch this debris with some fear, because this is where the next major disaster to hit the Earth could come from if our Moon does not cause it first.

Today the night sky is scrutinised continuously by thousands of amateur and professional astronomers from every part of the world so that nothing of interest goes unnoticed easily.

Drawing heavily upon the ever increasing amount of information from space carefully gathered over the years we can now begin to piece together, with some degree of confidence, the likely sequence of events that has led to the formation of our planet Earth.

Further Reading
Murdin P & Malin D *Catalogue of the Universe* Book Club Associates London 1980
Ronan C A *The Practical Astronomer* Bloomsbury Books London 1992
Kaufmann W J *Discovering the Universe* W H Freeman & Co New York 1990

CHAPTER THREE

BIRTH OF THE SUN

'He speaks to the sun and it does not shine; he seals off the light from the stars.' (Job 9:8)

The Primordial Solar Cloud

The Solar system began with the formation of an enormous cloud of the simplest forms of matter- hydrogen and helium gas. How this cloud became transformed into the very complex matter of the Sun and planets is the subject of the rest of this book. Hydrogen is by far the most abundant element in the Universe. There are probably billions of gigantic clouds of hydrogen still in existence throughout the rest of the Universe. We know that such clouds become compressed by their own gravity and eventually become stars.

When first formed, our own very special cloud of hydrogen which we will henceforward call the Primordial Solar Cloud, was roughly spherical in shape and billions of kilometres in diameter. It was extremely dense at the centre but this density decreased steadily with increasing distance away from the centre.

The cloud was not stationary. It moved through space at many thousands of kilometres per hour. In addition to this motion it and also slowly rotated about an axis through itself. This rotation was of crucial importance. Without it our planet would never have formed and we would not have night and day and seasons. All this is explained later on.

To explain the origin of the Primordial Solar Cloud we need to go back in time to the very beginning of the material Universe.

This takes us into a realm of much uncertainty and vast

amounts of money and time are still being spent to try and understand the origin of the material Universe. Two theories for the start of the Universe are considered in this book.

The first of these is the Big Bang Theory which is currently the most popular theory for the beginning of the material Universe. This theory is not without difficulties and does not give an acceptable explanation for moving and rotating clouds of hydrogen. Nevertheless a brief discussion of this theory is given in Appendix 1.

A new and previously unpublished theory for the start of the Universe which does explain how moving and rotating clouds of hydrogen were formed, is proposed and discussed in Appendix 2. This theory, called the Binary Particle Theory, describes how the Universe started with clouds of hydrogen which were brought into existence one by one over an infinite period of time.

Hydrogen is the simplest element from which all other elements can be formed so if we can explain the origin of hydrogen the formation of the rest of the elements and their combinations follows fairly readily.

As we need as a starting point for our story of the Earth's creation a vast moving and rotating cloud of hydrogen, the reader is left to decide whether the current Big Bang theory or the new Binary particle Theory offers the best explanation for the formation of such a cloud.

When the Primordial Solar Cloud was first formed its shape was more or less spherical with extremely high density hydrogen and other elements at its centre and very low density hydrogen at its outer edges. It was also very large - possibly twenty to forty billion kilometres in diameter depending on where its outer surface could be defined, and still subject to the 'wind' pressure from primordial cosmic particles (see Appendix 2). Like all other clouds it responded to this wind by beginning to rotate and float away like a gigantic balloon away from its point of origin exactly as Nature intended.

The story of how this Cloud eventually became the Solar System with a Sun and its retinue of planets is a rather long one which takes up the rest of this book. In this chapter we explain how the Primordial Solar Cloud first developed into a binary star system and how and why this binary star then collapsed into a single star we know today as the Sun.

Solar A and Solar B

When it drifted away from its point of origin the Primordial Solar Cloud was blown past possibly thousands of other galaxies like a giant ship drifting past islands until it eventually found a safe harbour in our Milky Way Galaxy (see Appendix 3). When it came within the region of space curved by the then mass of our galaxy it was captured by the gravitational pull of our galaxy and thus became part of it.

By this time the Cloud had gained much translational momentum, which is still preserved today and for this reason the entire Solar System is still hurtling at great speed and is very probably spiralling inwards towards the centre of the Milky Way Galaxy. As a result of its capture and as a result also of its initial rotation, the Primordial Solar Cloud by this stage had quite a complex rotation, as expected.

Rotation of the Cloud meant it had angular momentum. A simple illustration of angular momentum can be seen in a top that is set spinning on a smooth table which will go on spinning for quite a while because of its initial angular momentum. In the same way the Primordial Solar Cloud kept on rotating as the amount of friction in space was quite negligible.

Now momentum, like energy, is always conserved unless acted on by some external force. A spinning top only stops rotating because of frictional and air resistance. Out in space the Cloud was able to continue to rotate, but resisted only to a certain extent by the continued presence of the cosmic wind.

Gravitational forces within the Cloud were able to reduce the size of the Cloud but the angular momentum that the Cloud had so far acquired was preserved after contraction and the consequence of this was that as the Cloud began to contract it also began to rotate more rapidly. A simple illustration of this can be given. If children on a free wheeling merry-go-round got out of their outermost seats whilst it was in motion and took up seats near the centre the device would spin faster than before.

This rotation of the Primordial Solar Cloud was a vitally important factor. Without it the Cloud would have simply contracted by its own gravity into a single star and no planets would have formed. Many of the other hydrogen clouds in our galaxy have undoubtedly suffered this fate. But because the Cloud had a significant rotation the formation of a binary star became possible.

The rotation of the Cloud subjected it to strong centrifugal forces which, acting on their own, would normally have caused the Cloud to tear apart and become dispersed throughout the galaxy. But opposing this centrifugal force was the force of gravity which tended to make the Cloud smaller and more dense. In addition the Cloud was still buffeted by the cosmic wind which acted both with and against the two other forces on different parts of the cloud at different times. Under a combination of these forces the Cloud flattened into a disc which then fragmented into billions of rings. In time these rings contracted further into asteroids of frozen hydrogen and helium and other elements including iron. The origin of these elements is described in Appendix 4.

As contraction continued these asteroids then rearranged themselves into a bar shaped swarm. Finally the bar shaped swarm contracted into just two very dense and very large bodies rotating around each other about a common centre of

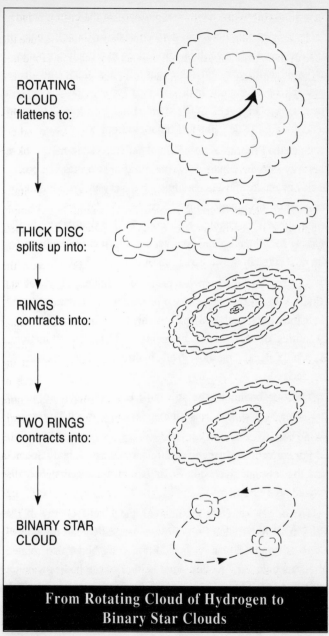

ROTATING
CLOUD
flattens to:

THICK DISC
splits up into:

RINGS
contracts into:

TWO RINGS
contracts into:

BINARY STAR
CLOUD

**From Rotating Cloud of Hydrogen to
Binary Star Clouds**

Fig. 3.1

form a binary system. These stages are illustrated in Figure 3.1.

Each body of this binary system consisted of a solid core of neutrons, iron and metallic hydrogen, an extremely deep ocean of liquid hydrogen and other gases and a thick and dense atmosphere of mainly hydrogen and helium gas above this 'ocean' (see Fig. A2.2). The name Binary Sun will be used henceforward to describe this binary system.

Once the Primordial Solar Cloud had become transformed in this way into the Binary Sun consisting of two massive bodies each not unlike the Planet Jupiter but very much larger, each member of this binary enjoyed a period of relative stability and tranquillity. This enabled each body in this double star in the making to tighten up and contract even further in readiness for the next stage in the construction of the Solar System.

As a result of the immense pressure within each body of the Binary Sun, and as a result also of numerous collisions during their formation, each body had by this time contained immense quantities of dust of all elements and their combinations. Appendix 4 explains how from hydrogen all other elements are derived.

The two bodies of the still dark Binary Sun were not of the same size as one was almost certainly much larger than the other.

For convenience we will call the more massive body Solar A and the less massive body Solar B and assume that Solar B rotated around Solar A.

The original angular momentum and kinetic energy of the Primordial Solar Cloud was now expressed by the rotation of Solar B around Solar A. In addition each body also rotated about its own axis. At this stage neither of the bodies was hot enough to emit heat and light but the temperature inside both was very high and still rising as a result of continued contraction and interaction.

Binary Stars

We digress a little now to consider binary stars in general.

A careful study of the stars in our Milky Way Galaxy reveals that most of them are not single ones but double ones and the term binary star is commonly applied to all double stars. Some triple or multiple stars are also present in our galaxy.

The formation of binary stars seems to be a characteristic of the behaviour of rotating gas clouds of all sizes, but binary systems can also form by chance as a result of the mutual gravitational attraction of two bodies which pass close enough to each other at just the right velocity. With hundreds of millions of stars being created and blown into space it is not surprising that in a few cases two stars were able to capture each other to form a binary star. Binary stars formed by mutual capture are more likely to be found in a disc shaped galaxy rather than in an irregular shaped galaxy, because in a disc close encounters between stars with just the right relative velocity should be fairly common. The closeness of the two components in any binary system formed by gravitational capture is dependant on the relative velocity of the two bodies at their closest approach. We have more to say on this point when the formation of the Earth/Moon Binary is discussed.

The number of binary and multiple star systems within our galaxy is unknown but is thought that at least 60% of all the observable stars in our galaxy are binary stars.

The estimate of binary stars in our galaxy is growing as our observations with increasingly powerful telescopes show that many stars previously thought to be single ones turn out to have one or more companions. In many binary systems only one of the components may be emitting light while the other has either not yet heated up sufficiently or gone past it and become a dark object that is impossible to detect by visual means. It may be that for a star to become light emitting it has to have a binary companion to warm it up to the required temperature for heat and light to be radiated and for this reason a large percentage of observable stars do have binary companions.

Binary systems in which both objects are dark and cold are virtually undetectable with the equipment we have at the moment, but should we develop a means of locating some of these dark matter objects in the Universe, we will undoubtedly find that our estimate of binary systems will increase even further.

The nearest star to us is Alpha Centauri. This is a binary star with two components A and B.

Alpha Centauri A weighs slightly more than our Sun and Alpha Centauri B weighs a little less than the Sun. The distance between these stars varies as they move around each other but at their closest encounter the distance is less than 2000 million kilometres, which is about the same as the distance between the Sun and the planet Saturn.

We may wonder why Alpha Centauri and other visual binaries appear to be stable and have not collapsed into a single star. The answer to this is that binary systems will remain stable for a very long time if the region around them is clear of gas and dust. If this is not the case then both components would increase in mass by sweeping up any matter in their path and thus the precarious balance will be upset and collapse would then become inevitable. Furthermore once a star becomes visible it begins to loose mass. This means that the gravitational force between them decreases and the two components become free to move away from each other. It is also difficult for a bright star to absorb mass from its surroundings because the powerful stream of subatomic particles (called the Solar wind for our Sun) blows away any gas or dust that may otherwise want to settle on it.

Hence if a binary star is going to collapse the most likely time for this to happen would be when the two components are still in the cold inactive stage and have not yet begun to radiate heat and light and when the surrounding region is still rich in gas and dust. Such conditions are likely to occur for example when two galaxies collide with each other.

Another star, again quite close to us, is a star called 61 Cygni. This is also a binary star, each component of which weighs about half that of the Sun. The distance between the components is about twice the distance between the Sun and the planet Pluto.

There are other binary stars in our galaxy which have components so close to each other that they cannot be made out as separate stars by even the best telescopes but are revealed by spectroscope. For example the binary star Mizar has a separation of about only 100 million miles which is about the same distance as that between the Earth and Sun. Such a binary system must be very close to collapse, and this could even happen within our lifetime, and we may even see the collapse and assume it to be a supernova explosion.

These few examples suggest that the idea that our Sun was once a binary star is entirely reasonable and is in accordance with what we know of other stars in our Galaxy. Whether our Binary Sun was formed from a single rotating cloud of hydrogen/helium or whether our Binary Sun was formed by one star capturing another as a result of a close encounter does not really matter because it is the collapse of this binary system which is all important.

Collapse of the Binary Sun

A binary star is a delicately balanced system, as can be imagined from its mode of formation. The two components really revolve around each other about a common centre of gravity, but where one body is much larger than the other it can be said that the smaller body orbits the larger one at a speed which is just right for its mass and distance apart. They exert a tug on each other continuously. If the gravitational tug is too small each body will spiral away in ever increasing circles and thus gain freedom from each other. If the tug is too great the bodies will spiral towards each other in ever decreasing circles and with increasing speed until they become involved in a shattering collision with each other.

Our planet Earth is part of a binary system, having as its companion the Moon so we have an excellent example on our doorstep to see how the components of a binary systems interact with each other. We are reminded of the effect the tug of the Moon's gravity on the Earth whenever we watch the ebb and flow of the tide on a beach. Less widely known is the fact that land masses on the Earth are also raised and lowered each day by the tug from the Moon and this, as we shall see, is responsible for some global catastrophes that have occurred on the Earth during the last few thousand years and further catastrophes for the same reason can be expected possibly in our lifetime.

If the Moon ran into a gigantic swarm of asteroids the Moon could easily be impeded in its orbit round the Earth in which case it would be deflected into an orbit closer to the Earth. If this happened it would move round the Earth faster. If it was unable to settle into a stable orbit again it would continue to spiral inwards towards the Earth moving faster each time round. Eventually it would approach the Earth very low in the horizon and travel at great speed almost half way round the world in only an hour or so at only a few thousand metres above ground level before breaking up in mid air and spilling its contents over nearly all the Earth's surface.

But this is not likely to happen because measurements indicate that our Moon is now receding away from us slowly which suggests that it is a recently captured satellite and is unlikely to collide with the Earth.

The collapse of the Binary Sun was not a sudden event but a fairly gradual one. In the Binary Sun the smaller body Solar B revolved round the larger body Solar A, but this rotation was not a stable one because both bodies were still growing and increasing in mass. With each revolution the distance between Solar A and Solar B decreased and the velocity of Solar B relative to Solar A increased.

When Solar B finally came very close to Solar A the gravitational attraction was so great that Solar B was torn apart into billions of very large and very dense fragments and particles of frozen gases.

Instead of taking, say three years, to complete one orbit round Solar A, Solar B now took only a few days to do so and then only a few hours. Finally the now fast moving fragments of Solar B plunged through the atmosphere and oceans of Solar A and was completely vaporised in the immense heat generated by the collision.

The collision, when it came, was thus between billions of dense fragments and frozen ices of Solar B and the disturbed atmosphere and ocean of Solar A.

Just before actual collision each fragment of Solar B had an extremely high velocity in a direction more or less horizontal to the surface of Solar A. Each fragment thus did not plunge vertically below the surface of Solar A, but at a very shallow angle. But as Solar B broke up first and hit Solar A at an angle the area affected by the collision was not circular as it would have been for a vertical 'head on' collision, but belt shaped, stretching in a wide band almost entirely round the equator of Solar A. Each of the billions of chunks of Solar A thus slid along and plunged deep into the liquid or solid surface of Solar B.

39

The heat generated by the billions of impacts and by friction as each high velocity chunk was brought to rest was enormous. The energy which Solar B had by virtue of its mass and velocity was mostly suddenly changed to heat energy, and the heat generated was sufficiently high to almost completely vaporise Solar B and a part of Solar A, thus forming a huge, extremely hot cloud of gas and dust. The cloud completely engulfed Solar A and rapidly expanded into a cloud some 10,000 million kilometres or more in diameter - such was the effect of the collision between Solar B and Solar A. See Fig. 4.1.

It is with this cloud that we will be concerned with in the rest of this book because from this the planets were formed. For this reason we will use the term Planetary Cloud to describe this cloud and we have much to say about it in the next two chapters.

Reasons for collapse of the Binary Sun

The actual reason why the Binary Sun collapsed is not known but we do know that collapses of binary stars are extremely common. Some astronomers now believe that there is one such collapse in our galaxy alone every 20 years and what is thought as being a supernova or exploding star by some astronomers is now believed by other astronomers to be a collapsing binary star.

There are at least four possible reasons why the Binary Sun collapsed and these are briefly discussed below.

Firstly the Binary Sun was formed as explained from a rotating cloud of hydrogen/helium gas. It is very likely that in the first contraction of the cloud not all the gas was used up so that a large proportion of the gas remained unused after the two main bodies Solar A and Solar B had formed. This unused gas then contracted as expected and formed a dense fog around both components of the Binary Sun which thus impeded rotational speeds and increased masses sufficiently to upset the balance.

Secondly our galaxy contains millions of clouds of hydrogen which have not as yet contracted into light emitting stars and forms part of the dark matter. This means that it is quite likely that the Binary Sun in its travels through the galaxy was in collision with one such cloud and this would have been enough to upset the precarious balance.

Thirdly there are in our galaxy some awesome objects called globular structures. These, as their name implies, are spherical objects and composed of thousands of closely packed stars, the combined mass of which is extremely large. They may be regarded as mini galaxies within our galaxy and are sometimes mistaken for a more distant spherical galaxies. They enjoy a somewhat rebellious orbit within our galaxy. Instead of following an orbit in one plane as the other stars do, these massive structures weave in and out of the galactic plane. There are believed to be at least 200 of these objects in our galaxy and the chances of a close encounter between one of these globular clusters and the Binary Sun could be rated as moderately high. Such an event would cause a serious interference in the gravitational field between the two components of the Binary Sun which would easily upset its delicate balance.

Fourthly our galaxy is a member of a cluster of galaxies. Collision between members of the same cluster are not unknown and the existence of spiral arms in our galaxy suggest that our galaxy has been involved in a collision with another galaxy from our own cluster. Observations carried out by Astronomers suggest that the spiral arms of a galaxy are locations where there is an accumulation of gas and dust and the gas and dust in these regions is able to contract to form new stars quite quickly. Thus the Binary Sun may have also had access to a fresh supply of gas and dust and as a result of this the mass of each component would increase and also the orbital rotation of one component about the other would be impeded

41

and lead to a reduction in the centrifugal force. For one or more or all of the reasons given above the mass or velocity of one or both of the two components of the Binary Sun was altered to a point at which the delicate balance was upset and a catastrophic but, fortunate for us, collapse ensued.

Further Reading
Bok B *Early Phases of Star Formation* Sky & Telescope April 1981
Taylor S R *Solar System Evolution* Cambridge University Press1992
Ashbrook J *Visual Double Stars for the Amateur* Sky & Telescope November 1980
Noyes R *The Sun our Star* Harvard University Press 1982Chapter 4

CHAPTER FOUR

ORIGIN OF THE SOLAR NEBULA

'The heavens declare the glory of God:the skies proclaim the work of his hands (Ps. 19:1)

Theories for the formation of the Solar System

The theory advanced in this book is that the planets of the Solar System were formed from the Planetary Cloud which was created when the Binary Sun collapsed as described in Chapter 3.

In this chapter we explain some important features of the Cloud.

But first it is of some interest and relevance to take a brief look of some of the many other theories that have been proposed over the centuries to explain how the Solar system was formed.

These theories can be broadly classified under four headings termed Turbulence, Tidal, Nebula and Accumulation.

Turbulence theories

Descartes (1644) is credited for the first version of the Turbulence Theory. This theory postulates that there was once a rotating and turbulent atmosphere of gas stretching for billions of kilometres round the newly formed Sun and that this atmosphere eventually condensed somehow into the planets.

The reason for this turbulent atmosphere is not clearly given, although we now know that such a cloud of gas could have existed for a short period of time in the last stages of the contraction of a rotating cloud of gas soon after the main body of the Sun had formed. This is because of a vortex effect of the sort observed when water flows down a sinkhole. In this case the 'sinkhole' is the gravitational pull of the newly formed Sun and the remnants of gas that had not as yet become absorbed into the Sun became the rotating turbulent atmosphere.

A large rotating cloud of gas will rotate faster as the cloud contracts under its own gravity so that what we really see in a vortex is an illustration of the conservation of angular momentum when a volume of gas has to rotate faster as it converges inwards, and it is this rapid rotation that may have led Descartes to assume that our Sun once had a turbulent rotating atmosphere.

Turbulence theories do not explain much but have served their purpose in drawing attention to the possibility of the existence of a rotating cloud of gas round a Sun that had already been formed and this feature is used in the new theory advanced later on in this book.

Tidal theories

Georges Louis de Buffon (1785) proposed the first of the Tidal theories which postulate that a cloud of gas and dust called the Solar Nebula was caused by a collision between a massive comet and the Sun. This theory agrees closely with what is proposed in this book but de Buffon did not consider in detail the consequences of an impact between a massive comet and the Sun and in any case he did not have the benefit of the vast amount of knowledge about the Solar System that we have today.

The Tidal theory was later developed by James Jeans and Harold Jeffreys who proposed that the Solar Nebula was caused not by a collision but a close approach of another star to the Sun. The approaching star is thought to have raised a tide of material from the Sun and tore it away. The material torn away from the Sun is then thought to have formed the planets but important details of how this happened are not given. This theory also contains similarities with what is proposed later in this book.

The idea that one massive body can tear off a chunk from another body without actually colliding with it is one that we will use in a different context as a basis for explaining some of the physical features of the Earth and we will return to this point later.

Nebula Theories

The Nebula Theory for the formation of the Solar System was proposed by Kant (1755) and Laplace (1796). This theory postulates the existence of a large rotating cloud of gas and dust from which both the Sun and the planets were thought to have been formed but no mention as to the origin of the Nebula is made and the theory has been discredited for several reasons that need not be given here.

Accumulation theories

The modern theory which is believed by some to be very promising is called The Accumulation Theory. This theory postulates that the Solar System was formed from a slowly rotating gas cloud which was originally composed mainly of hydrogen but managed to mop up and accumulate interstellar dust ejected in supernova explosions from massive stars that had come to the end of their lives.

Once the dust cloud was formed, the theory suggests, the cloud then collapsed into the Sun and its planets as a result of a shock wave from yet another supernova. Again precise details as to how this happened are not given. Even this modern theory leaves many questions unanswered and does not tell us very much about how our planet was made. The only feature that can be used from this theory is the idea that the cloud had an accumulation of useful planetary making dust but the theory advanced in this book for the origin of this dust is that most of the elements did not result from supernova explosions of distant stars but were created within our own star the Sun mainly as a result of its collision with its once binary companion. See Appendix 4.

Although all the existing theories for the Solar System briefly described above are unsatisfactory for one reason or another they all have all helped in the quest of the truth and as such have served their purpose.

The theory for the formation of the planets that is proposed in this book has not (to the best of the author's knowledge) been previously published but follows in a logical way from the idea of the collapse of the Binary Sun. This new theory gives satisfactory answers to all of the many problems about the Solar System that have puzzled astronomers for some time and may be used to give satisfactory explanations for most, if not all, the many problems about our Solar System, and the rest of this book demonstrates this.

Features of the Planetary Cloud

To understand how the planets were formed from the Planetary Cloud we must first consider three very important features of the Cloud. These were its rotation, its temperature distribution and the forces that acted within it.

Rotation of the Planetary Cloud

All of the theories previously proposed for the Solar System postulate the idea of a slow rotating cloud to begin with but none of the theories make it clear why the cloud rotated.

Without rotation no planets could have been formed as the Cloud would then have contracted back into the Single Sun.

The reason for this rotation goes back to how the Cloud was formed. The event that gave birth to the Planetary Cloud was the collapse of the Binary Sun. This was not a direct collision but a rotational collision between two cold, massive and dark spheres of mainly hydrogen that rotated about each other (see Fig.4.1.). It is important to stress that the collision was a spiralling of one body (Solar B) inwards towards the other (Solar A) so that Solar B skimmed along the surface of Solar B and disintegrated before it became deeply embedded in Solar A. On contact millions of fragments of both Solar A and Solar B screeched and scraped their way almost half way round Solar A before becoming completely vaporised.

Before the collapse the two components of the Binary Sun rotated about each other around a common centre of gravity and hence locked in the system was a very substantial amount of angular momentum. We can trace the origin of this momentum right back to the rotation that existed in the cloud from which the Binary Sun was formed in the first place.

In a frictionless system angular momentum is never lost. The rotation of the components of the Binary Sun was not entirely frictionless because of the presence of gas and the cosmic ray bombardment but nevertheless most of the angular momentum that the Binary Sun had before its collapse was transferred, after collapse, to the rotation of the now Single Sun and the rotation of the Planetary Cloud.

Immediately after the collapse of the Binary Sun the Planetary Cloud that was formed faithfully held on to much of the angular momentum and rotated very rapidly around the now single but still darkened Sun.

As this Cloud expanded the average rate of rotation decreased but the total angular momentum remained unchanged. As the

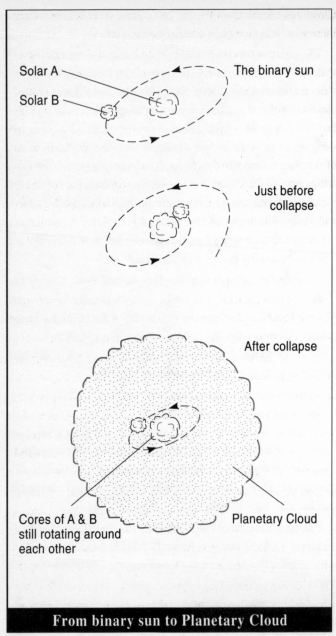

From binary sun to Planetary Cloud

Fig. 4.1

Cloud contracted again the rate of rotation increased but again there was little change in angular momentum.

The rotation is perhaps easier to understand if we remember that in the Solar System today 99% of the total angular momentum is concentrated on the planets and the rotation of the Sun itself only accounts for a small proportion of it. This fact has puzzled Astronomers in the past but once the origin of the Planetary Cloud as described is understood the distribution of angular momentum is as expected and suggests that one component of the Binary Sun (Solar B) was almost completely vaporised as it scraped its way along the surface of the other and some of its angular momentum preserved in the rotation of the resulting Planetary Cloud.

Temperatures in the Planetary Cloud

It has long been recognised that the Cloud from which the planets were formed must have been a hot one, but again few attempts have been made to explain the source of the heat.

In the collapse of the Binary Sun some of the huge amount of kinetic energy that the system had prior to its collapse was instantly converted to heat energy.

The amount of heat generated was so great that the temperature attained was sufficient not only to vaporise parts of both Solar A and Solar B but also to alter existing elements and form new elements as described in Appendix 4.

The temperature on the collision surfaces of the surviving component (Solar A) was initially large enough to become a source of intense heat radiation which caused the expanding Planetary Cloud to be continuously kept hot and be supplied with newly vaporised material for some time after the collapse. The Planetary Cloud was thus intensely and uniformly hot when first formed with an initial temperature of millions of degrees.

49

This initial temperature had to be very large. Temperature is really a measure of particle velocity and if the temperature was not high enough after the collapse, most of the vaporised material caused by the collision would not have had the energy to escape from the combined gravity of the two colliding bodies and would have fallen back on to it and no planets would have formed. On the other hand if the temperature was too great then all the material in the Cloud would have escaped and dispersed into space and again no planets would have been formed.

But the temperature was such that some material fell back on the now Single Sun and some material escaped to the very outer boundaries of the Solar System where it still lies. This material is still slowly returning to the Sun and we have much to say about this 'escaped' material in the final chapter of this book.

Some debris thrown up by the Binary Sun collapse neither fell back on to the Sun nor escaped altogether but became trapped in between these two extremes and it is this debris only which later evolved into the known planets of our Solar System.

It is very fortunate for us, and this must be stressed, that a very substantial amount of vaporised material did not have the necessary energy to either make an escape or become part of the Planetary Cloud. This material fell back on to the combined Sun and effectively sealed it for a while. As we will see later in this book this too was according to Nature's plan and was an important event, otherwise life on Earth would never have been able to start.

Intense heat was necessary to propel a good proportion of the very fine dust and gas molecules and give them just sufficient velocity to get to where they did billions of kilometres away from the now single but still darkened and now dormant Sun.

While the inner parts of the Planetary Cloud immediately around the dormant Sun remained very hot for some time, the heat was radiated away into space. Thus in the course of time a temperature gradient developed so that near the dormant Sun the temperature dropped to a few thousand degrees, but some 10,000 million or so kilometres away the temperature was scarcely above absolute zero. There was a thus a gradual variation of temperature which dropped by only a degree or two for every million kilometres away from the dormant Sun.

This temperature variation is an important feature of the Planetary Cloud as it explains why the planets are so different from each other in composition and atmosphere. All this is explained in greater detail later on.

Forces acting within the Cloud

Every tiny particle within the Planetary Cloud was subject to four forces - centrifugal, gravitational and magnetic and the solar and cosmic winds. The planets were formed as a result of a subtle combination of these four forces.

Centrifugal forces

We consider first the centrifugal force.

The planets were formed only from the material that did not either fall back on to the dormant Sun or escape into the outermost regions of the Solar System. The material in the Planetary Cloud must therefore have had just the right finely balanced velocity to be able to orbit the dormant Sun.

This only became possible when the centrifugal force acting outwards on the particle was exactly balanced by gravitational forces acting inwards.

Thus only those particles with exactly the required centrifugal force remained in the Planetary Cloud - the rest of the particles were either dispersed into the outermost regions of the Solar System or reclaimed quickly by the still dark and dormant Sun.

Gravitational forces

Gravity operates between any two bodies with mass and acts to bring the two bodies together. In the Cloud each tiny particle may be considered to be one of the bodies and the dormant Sun as the other body.

If gravity was the only force that operated in the Cloud then each particle would move in a direction towards very near the centre of the dormant Sun. Gravity acting alone would have led to a uniform contraction of the Cloud and thus all individual particles within the Cloud would have been forced closer together as the Cloud contracted.

Magnetic forces

We know that if a current is passed through a coil wound round a bar of magnetic material the bar becomes magnetised. Something like this happened within the Planetary Cloud. Within the Cloud there was an abundance of iron, cobalt and nickel and other magnetic particles. A fierce spray of electrons from the dormant Sun acted like an electric current and caused some of these particles in the Cloud to become magnetised and behave like tiny little magnets.

Particles with magnetic properties became attracted to these tiny magnets and a sorting of magnetic and non magnetic material then took place. Magnetic particles began to clump together as soon as temperatures were low enough to allow this to happen.

Solar wind and Cosmic ray bombardment

Even today our planet is relentlessly bombarded by cosmic rays and had it not been for our atmosphere these rays would have long killed us all. Cosmic rays acted on the each particle in the Planetary Cloud. This force on each particle was a transient one but sufficient to jostle each particle into separation from other particles to which they may have become illegally stuck to by weak gravitational forces, and so like rain through a cloud of dust, the cosmic rays made sure that each particle took its rightful place within the Cloud in equilibrium with the other three forces.

The Solar wind from the dormant Sun acted in a similar way. This wind was extremely fierce to begin with, but as more and more debris fell back to the sun, this had the effect of gradually reducing its intensity.

The very strong Solar wind was responsible for propelling particles out into space in the first instance.

Today we can still see the power of the Solar wind whenever a giant asteroid comes close to the Sun and is bombarded by the Solar wind which blows and vapourises parts of the asteroid, giving it a characteristic tail and the whole becomes a comet.

How these forces combined to form the planets is explained fully in the next chapter.

Size of the Planetary Cloud

Our Planetary Cloud has long disappeared and what is left of it is only a small part which became transformed into the planets and comets and asteroids of the Solar System.

The orbit of the outermost planet Pluto does not really define the size of the original Cloud. There is debris from the Binary Sun collapse that still lies beyond Pluto and this material may still be aggregating to form planet like bodies so there may be other planets beyond Pluto.

We can get a better understanding of the size of the Planetary Cloud by studying some of the thousands of comets that orbit the Sun today in orbits much greater in size than that of the outermost planet.

The Nebular expands at about 900km per second

The Crab Pulsar at the centre of the Nebular rotates 30 times each second

The Crab Nebula

Fig. 4.2

54

The short period comets are natural consequences of the collapse of the Binary Sun. They are simply parts of the Planetary Cloud which have condensed and formed into asteroids containing a large proportion of volatile material. They have predictable orbits round the Sun and most of these will end up by either crashing on to one of the planets or the Sun.

Some of the long period comets - those that have huge highly elliptical orbits were probably not formed by the collapse of the Binary Sun but are almost certainly left over bits from the cloud from which the Binary Sun was formed in the first place. But other long period comets are manifestations of the debris that was thrown out after the Binary Sun collapsed.

With powerful telescopes and computational facilities we can now make sufficient observations to be able to plot the huge orbits of some of the short and long period comets. If this was done and the results plotted and superimposed on each other we would be able to get some idea of the size of the Planetary Cloud.

Such an exercise could be carried out by computer modelling. If we displayed the orbits of all known comets simultaneously on a VDU screen this would give us an image looking like a ball of tangled string or like a swarm of bees round their disturbed hive.

The Crab Nebula

Our Planetary Cloud has now almost disappeared but we have another cloud to look at to give us some idea of what ours was like.

About a thousand years ago (in July 1054) Chinese astronomers noticed a very bright light which appeared suddenly in the constellation of Taurus. This light stayed bright for a few days before becoming completely enveloped in a huge cloud of gas and dust that rapidly expanded and has continued to expand to this day. This cloud is still visible in the night sky and is known as the Crab Nebula because of its crab like shape.

Although astronomers cite this as an example of a supernova or exploding star there is good evidence to suggest that the Crab Nebula was formed as a result of the collapse of a binary system in exactly the same way as our own Planetary Cloud was formed.

Astronomers have recognised that so called supernova or exploding stars are particularly common in close binary systems. The idea that what is observed is not a supernova but a collision between two massive bodies seems not to have received much attention although this is a natural consequence, of close binaries in a gas rich environment.

If we accept that the Crab Nebula is the result of a collapsed binary we have a very good model for what our own Planetary Cloud must have looked like in size and shape during its early stages.

The gases and dust in the Crab Nebula are currently expanding at about nine hundred metres per second and its size today is about thirty thousand million kilometres across its largest dimension. These figures are based on an estimation of the distance of the Crab Nebula from the Earth. If our estimation of this distance is correct this would make the Crab Nebula about two or three times larger than our Planetary Nebula.

One of the interesting features of the Crab Nebula is that it behaves like a huge cyclotron which causes the ions and electrons in the gaseous material to move in large magnetic orbits. The existence of a magnetic field in a nebula is particularly interesting and relevant to the creation of the Solar System. We describe later on how magnetic material and magnetic forces led to the formation of the core of all planets so evidence of magnetism in the Crab Nebula is encouraging.

At the centre of the Crab Nebula is a source of strong radiation not unlike the Solar wind and observations suggest that the Nebula hides a small but very massive object that is rotating very rapidly. This implies that the binary collapse in this case involved a collision between two objects and the remnants of one object is now still rapidly rotating round the other one by virtue of the angular momentum it had before the collapse.

The Crab Nebula may thus be regarded as a model of the Planetary Cloud. In time the outer edges of the Nebula will go on expanding into space and will be dispersed but the inner regions will cool and then pick up some of the rotation already at the centre. When this happens the remnants of the Crab Nebula will sort itself out into a planetary system not unlike our own. But not in our lifetime.

Having given a description of the Planetary Cloud in this chapter we can now proceed to give a broad outline of how the Solar System was formed from this Cloud and this is done in the next chapter.

Further Reading
Falk S & Schramm D *Did the Solar System Start with a Bang?* Sky & Telescope July 1979
Reeves H *The Origin of the Solar System* Mercury March/April 1977
Frazier K *The Solar System* Time-Life Books 1995
Kaufmann W J *Discovering the Universe* W H Freeman & Co New York 1990

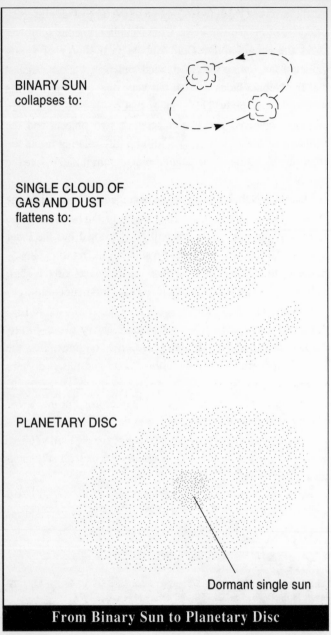

BINARY SUN
collapses to:

SINGLE CLOUD OF
GAS AND DUST
flattens to:

PLANETARY DISC

Dormant single sun

From Binary Sun to Planetary Disc

Fig. 5.1

CHAPTER FIVE

FROM SOLAR NEBULA
TO SOLAR SYSTEM

'... them also that burned incense .. to the sun, and to the
moon, and to the planets... ' (2 Kin. 23:5)

Six stages of creation

The Solar System was formed from the very hot and turbulent
Planetary Cloud and to understand how this happened we need
to consider logically how the Cloud cooled, contracted,
condensed into asteroids and finally aggregated into planets.

Although all of the existing theories for the Solar System
assume a cloud of gas and dust to begin with, little attention
appears to have been paid to the origin of the cloud and the
precise manner in which this cloud changed into the planets.

This is a very important aspect of the Earth's creation because
almost all of the physical features of the Earth that we see today
can be traced back to the manner in which the Earth and each
planet was formed and very little has changed since then.
Contrary to general opinion the surface of the Earth has hardly
altered since its creation and the evidence for the manner in
which it was created is all around us at the present time. For this
reason it is essential to consider the change from Cloud to planet
in a logical step by step manner-something which other theories
have failed to do.

The transformation from the Planetary Cloud to the Solar
System was a fairly straightforward and natural process and can
best be described in six stages as follows.

Stage 1 .... Formation of the Planetary Disc

Stage 2 .... Formation of rings of dust and gas

Stage 3 .... Formation of asteroids

Stage 4 .... Formation of iron/metallic hydrogen cores

Stage 5 .... Formation of planets

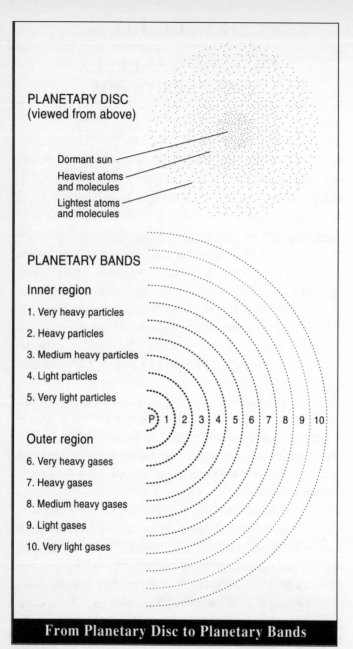

PLANETARY DISC
(viewed from above)

Dormant sun
Heaviest atoms
and molecules
Lightest atoms
and molecules

PLANETARY BANDS

Inner region

1. Very heavy particles

2. Heavy particles

3. Medium heavy particles

4. Light particles

5. Very light particles

P 1 2 3 4 5 6 7 8 9 10

Outer region

6. Very heavy gases

7. Heavy gases

8. Medium heavy gases

9. Light gases

10. Very light gases

From Planetary Disc to Planetary Bands

Fig. 5.2

Stage 6 .... Dormant Sun to Burning Sun

These stages are described below.

Stage 1 The Planetary Disc

When first formed the Planetary Cloud was a rapidly expanding cloud of irregular shape not unlike the Crab Nebula.

A significant amount of material in the Cloud did not have the necessary velocity to escape very far from the gravitational pull of the dormant Sun and this material soon fell back on to it and the dormant sun became covered by a thick atmosphere of dust containing heavy elements, notably iron and its oxides.

At this stage the dormant Sun was really quite a complex dynamic system but an observer at Earth distance would have seen it as a huge, faintly glowing but not bright, sphere of gas and dust about four or five times its present diameter.

The fall back of material onto the huge dormant Sun was a fortunate and essential step, because it meant that the rest of the Planetary Cloud was partially but not fully protected from the solar wind which started almost immediately after the collapse. We will return to this wind later on in this chapter.

As a result of gravitational, centrifugal and wind forces the irregularities in the shape of the Planetary Cloud soon evened out and the cloud became less crab like and more spherical. The cloud began to contract, and as it did so the rotational speed of the Cloud increased dramatically so as to retain all its original angular momentum.

Under the continued influence of the same forces the now spherical Cloud gradually flattened to a disc not unlike in shape to the Milky Way Galaxy. This disc marked a very important stage in the transformation of the Cloud into planets and the term Planetary Disc will be used for it in the descriptions that follow.

To give some idea of size, we can surmise that at one stage the Disc was about five million kilometres thick and about six billion kilometres in diameter, rotating like an enormous wheel with the darkened and dormant Sun at the hub. The average density of the disc was very low - only about one teaspoonful of very fine dust per cubic metre of space. See Fig. 5.1.

Within this enormous Disc were countless trillions of atoms of every possible kind formed by the processes of fusion and spallation and molecules of every form of matter formed by chemical combinations of the atoms. The disc was still continuously bombarded by cosmic rays and a subdued but still powerful solar wind as if to ensure that atoms not quite in their right place within the disc would be nudged along until they became fixed in their rightful place within the Disc.

As the Disc contracted even further every tiny particle within it was also influenced by the centrifugal and gravitational forces. Under these forces the heaviest particles of material found themselves congregating in the inner regions of the disc closest to the dormant Sun while the lightest particles found themselves thrown to the outer regions of the Disc. In between these extremes there was a gradual variation of particle mass so that particles became sorted by mass alone and found their rightful place in the disc. Thus concentrations of particles having similar masses formed and distinct bands of material began to appear in the Disc. This is illustrated in Fig 5.2.

Stage 2 Rings of dust and gas

With the reduction in intensity of the Solar wind the Planetary Disc was able to contract steadily and hence tightened up around the dormant Sun and the density of the Disc was thus able to increase.

This contraction took its time and during this time the Disc was once again able to sort itself into a banded structure as shown in Figure 5.2.

The figure shows an Inner Region near the dormant Sun and an Outer Region away from the dormant Sun. Both these regions can be described as follows.

Inner Region

When the Planetary Cloud was first formed there was much material which consisted of the heavier elements and their chemical combinations. Much of this material did not have the necessary velocity to get far enough from the dormant Sun and was thus attracted back towards the dormant Sun where it formed a thick and dense dust cloud consisting of all kinds of elements and minerals but especially the stable high melting point oxides of iron and silica. The reader is reminded that iron and silica were among the elements formed in great abundance by the fusion process discussed in Appendix 4.

For this reason the Inner Region of the Disc consisted of fine dust particles of many kinds which remain solid and only melt into liquids and vaporise into gases at very high temperatures.

Without too much disturbance from the dormant Sun the solid dust particles within this Inner Region were able to sort themselves out according to particle mass with the heaviest particles closest to the dormant Sun and grading into the lightest particles away from the dormant Sun. In this way hundreds of bands of different kinds of dust were formed and although there was a very gradual gradation of the particles between bands we can for convenience group them into five bands as follows

Band 1........... Very heavy particles

eg Feldspar, Hornblende, Clay Minerals

Band 2........... Heavy particles

eg Magnetite, Clay minerals

Band 3............ Medium heavy particles

eg calcite, halite, gypsum, hematite

Band 4........... Light particles

eg quartz, iron

Band 5........... Very light particles

eg carbon, sulphur

It is important to remember that hydrogen and water were available in great abundance throughout the Planetary Cloud and Disc, so that all the five bands mentioned above also had copious supplies of these in addition to the minerals named.

As the Planetary disc continued to contract each of these bands then subdivided again into hundreds of rings where the particles having the same mass became concentrated.

The breathtaking beautiful rings of the Planet Saturn give us a wonderful insight into how the rings of the early solar system may have looked. Saturn's rings may thus be regarded as a small scale model of the early stages of the Solar System and we will return to these rings and their formation when we come to describe this planet and other planets in Appendices 6 - 8.

The Outer Region

This part of the Planetary Disc consisted mainly of gases of many different kinds, most of which were also formed by the fusion process when the Binary Sun collapsed.

The temperature in this outer region of rarefied gases and dust had dropped to near absolute zero, so that this part of the Disc was made up with very tiny specks of snow and ice made up from frozen gases of all kinds.

Despite the very tiny size of each particle in this region gravitational, centrifugal and cosmic ray forces were still able to divide this region into bands as with the Inner Region.

Five bands may again be identified as follows working outwards from the outermost band of the Inner region.

Band 6 .... Very Heavy gases

eg Chlorine, Sulphur Dioxide

Band 7........... Heavy gases

eg Carbon Dioxide

Band 8........... Medium gases

eg Oxygen, Nitrogen

Band 9............ Light gases

eg Neon, Methane, Ammonia, Water vapour

Band 10..........Very light gases

eg Hydrogen, Helium

In the outer subregion at one extreme, farthest away from the dormant Sun, only the lightest gases like Hydrogen and Helium were found in abundance. On the other extreme of this region nearer the dormant Sun only the more heavy gases like Sulphur Dioxide had accumulated. There is a linear relationship between the molecular weights of the above gases and their position in the Outer Region. Again it should be stressed that abundantly available hydrogen and water vapour were also present in each of the bands as expected.

As the Planetary Disc contracted the bands of gases again subdivided into hundreds of rings. Each ring differed from its neighbour only by the slightly different proportion of one of the gases of the bands described above, so that the outermost ring, for example, consisted almost entirely of hydrogen and helium whereas the innermost ring consisted of very little hydrogen and helium but was rich in the heavy gases like Sulphur Dioxide.

Stage 3 Asteroids by the billion

With all the material in the Planetary Disc now concentrated into rings of dust and gas it was a simple matter for the process of planet building to commence.

The dormant Sun exerted a strong gravitational tug on each ring of dust and gas and the result of this was a contraction and increase in density of each ring. As this happened tiny particles of dust clumped together to form larger particles the size of sand grains. Further contraction led to more clumping together and so pebble and eventually cobble size aggregations were formed. These in turn clumped again to form boulders and finally into small and large asteroids.

This went on not only in the Inner Regions of the Planetary Disc but also in the outer Regions where asteroids made from ices of many kinds were formed.

It has to be stressed that as the aggregations of dust and gas grew bigger and heavier they began to spiral inwards gradually towards the centre of the Planetary Disc, growing all the time as they did so. Eventually asteroids of all shapes and sizes were thus formed. This tended to upset the order of the rings a little as asteroids spiralled their way from outer rings to inner rings. A good proportion of these asteroids are still wandering about in the Solar System seemingly in search of more particles to mop up and attempting to find a resting place. We have more to say about these wandering asteroids in the final chapter of this book.

Stage 4 Iron and metallic hydrogen cores

As shown in Figure 5.2 iron was one of the lightest elements in the Inner region of the Planetary Disc and being formed by the fusion process there was abundant supply of it throughout the Disc but the amount of iron was particularly high in Band 4 and a little less in Band 5 and Band 3.

Now it is a well known fact that if an electric current is passed through around a piece of iron it becomes magnetised. A flow of electrons may be regarded as a flow of an electric current and the Planetary Disc was subject to the Solar and Cosmic wind which included electrons. Thus the very tiny fragments of iron throughout the entire Disc became magnetised.

Now the magnetic attraction between particles is thousands of times greater than the gravitational attraction. The result of this magnetism was that the iron and other magnetic material in the bands and rings of the Planetary disc aggregated first and the very tiny particles grew very rapidly. Atoms thus quickly found partners and became molecules which clumped together to form specs of iron dust. These in turn grew to the size of little round balls like mustard seeds and so on to larger

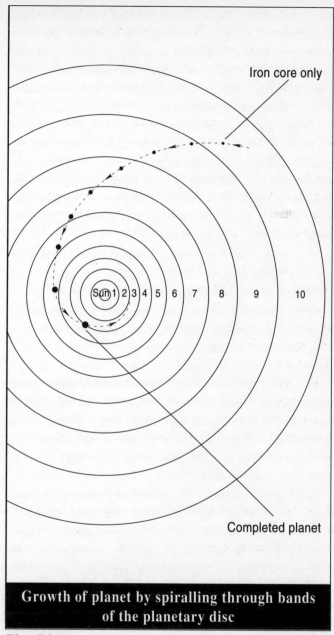

Growth of planet by spiralling through bands of the planetary disc

Fig. 5.3

concentrations the size of pebbles and boulders several meters in diameter and then into small and giant asteroids. As these concentrations grew in size and mass they could no longer stay in the ring of their formation but moved inwards in the Disc and began to sweep up all the iron and magnetic material that came within their now very powerful magnetism.

On their journey through the Planetary Disc they not only swept up iron and other magnetic material from other rings but in doing so also acquired all the angular momentum that these particles had by virtue of being in orbit round the dormant Sun. This meant that as the iron asteroids grew in size they also began to rotate about their own axis which was at right angles to the plane of the Planetary Disc.

The iron asteroids thus grew in size into spheres very rapidly and this process continued until most of the iron in the Planetary disc had been neatly gathered up.

As the Planetary Disc became even smaller and denser the spheres of iron were then able to attract each other and grow even larger until finally only about twenty or thirty massive spherical bodies of iron (and other magnetic material) were formed. These bodies were of different sizes and rotated around the dormant Sun in slightly different orbits. Bearing in mind that these bodies had by now spiralled a long way towards the dormant Sun they had also gathered up all the angular momentum of the particles from which they were composed and rotated very rapidly.

Some of the solid iron spheres went on to become the foundation cores of planets but many of the others did not do so.

One such sphere is only a few thousand kilometres below our feet at this moment and we call this particular body the Core of the Earth. Another small one crash landed on to the Earth in Greece and a third can be seen near the surface of the Planet Jupiter. We will return to these three rather special iron spheres later on in the book.

Hydrogen was widely available throughout the Planetary Disc and for this reason iron particles and asteroids became covered over with frozen hydrogen. Thus for the innermost planets the core is made almost entirely from iron, but for the outermost planets the core is made from almost entirely neutrons and frozen hydrogen and each planet is likely to have different amounts of iron and metallic hydrogen in their cores.

Stage 5 Formation of the planets

As explained above the first stage in the formation of the planets from all the material in the Planetary Disc was the formation of spherical iron or iron/metallic hydrogen cores. These ranged in size from only a few to hundreds of kilometres in diameter and being made of magnetic material were very highly magnetic, acquiring a magnetic North Pole and a magnetic South Pole by virtue of their axis of rotation which was a right angles to the Planetary Disc and the direction of the wind of electrons flowing outwards from the dormant Sun.

While the cores were being formed the rest of the material in the rings of the Planetary disc had by this time also aggregated into clumps ranging in size from a few microns to several hundred metres.

Because the mass and velocity of the cores changed all the time, they were forced to spiral inwards in the Disc and in doing came into contact with the dust and asteroids formed in the rings. In this way the naked cores were subject to intense asteroid bombardment and encounters with clouds of thick dust and thus became coated in layer upon layer of crashed asteroids and dust. At any given point in time the nature of crashed asteroids or dust layer was predominantly of the type expected in the ring the spiralling embryonic planet found itself in.

This spiralling in went on for some time and eventually the cores were completely covered over. This process went on and on and in this way each core acquired layer upon layer and thus became transformed into spheres ranging in size from a few hundred kilometres to a few thousand kilometres. Thus a few large planets and possibly hundreds of much smaller baby planets came into existence.

Possibly twenty or thirty large planets were formed in this way but only the nine we see in the Solar System have survived to this day. The rest either spiralled all the way back to the dormant Sun or else were involved in collisions with each other to form bigger planets. We will return to this point in Appendices 6 - 8 where each of the existing planets are examined and evidence of planet to planet collision is discussed.

Long after the planets had formed as described above some of the planets acquired atmospheres. This atmosphere may be regarded as nothing more than the final layer to be aggregated and was acquired by each planet in a slightly different way. Instead of the growing planet moving into a ring of material and acquiring this material, the newly formed planet had now settled into an orbit that suited its mass and was therefore unable to move in any further.

But as the intensity of the Solar wind became less the contraction of the rings of gases in the Outer region continued and the newly made planets found themselves in orbit for a short while in one or more of the rings of gases. In this way the planets acquired different atmospheres and a more detailed explanation of this for each planet in turn is given in Appendices 6 - 8.

Stage 6 Dormant Sun to Burning Sun

The Sun is the nearest star to us and as such we know enough about it to warrant a separate chapter. How our Sun was transformed from a dormant and dark object to a wonderful source of tremendous heat and brilliant light is explained in Appendix 5.

Explaining the Solar system

Any theory for the Solar System must give a satisfactory explanation for a certain number of well established facts. The Binary Sun theory described in this and the previous chapter satisfies five well established facts that we do know about the planets and these are listed and discussed below.

Firstly the planets revolve round the Sun in the same direction in elliptical but almost circular orbits that lie nearly in the same plane. This fact is explained by the new idea that the Planetary Cloud had a rotation about the dormant Sun by virtue of the method by which the cloud was formed and this enabled the cloud to become egg shaped and finally into a flat elliptical shape. Galaxies change shape for the same reason and this is explained in Appendix 3. Computer models confirm this pattern.

Secondly seven of the nine planets rotate about their axes in the same direction (anticlockwise) as their orbit round the Sun. This is as expected because the two components of the Binary Sun also rotated about each other in an anticlockwise direction. This rotation really started when the Cloud from which the Binary Sun evolved was first formed.

As all the original angular momentum was in an anticlockwise direction some of this momentum was also preserved in the rotation of individual planets which captured and retained the angular momentum of the crashed asteroids. Thus the direction of the rotation of each planet supports the theory that the planets were built up from orbiting dust and asteroids as explained. There are however two notable exceptions to this rule which affect two of the planets and the reasons for these become clear when these two planets are described in greater detail in Appendices 6, 7 and 8.

Thirdly the Sun makes up 99.9% of the mass of the Solar System but appears to have only has 1% of the angular momentum. This is as expected because the original angular momentum was due only to the rotation of one of the components of the

71

Binary Sun about the other which subsequently collided and partly vaporised to form the Planetary Cloud. Hence the apparent deficiency of angular momentum in the Sun lends support to the binary collapse theory. A vast amount of angular momentum is preserved inside the sun but has not previously been considered. Appendix 5 explains why this is so.

Fourthly there are two groups of planets. The inner group consisting of the four terrestrial planets Mercury, Venus, Earth and Mars are small but have a high density. The second group of planets are the giant planets Jupiter, Saturn, Uranus and Neptune which have low densities. This is in complete accord with the theory outlined above where the denser material of the Planetary Cloud stayed closer to the dormant Sun than the lighter material. The average density of each planet has been estimated and is given below.

Planet	Density (water = 1.0)	Planet	Density (water = 1.0)
1. Mercury	5.4	6. Jupiter	1.3
2. Venus	5.2	7. Saturn	0.7
3. Earth	5.5	8. Uranus	1.3
4. Mars	3.9	9. Neptune	1.6
5. Asteroid Ceres	2.3	10. Pluto	0.5?

This table confirms that as we go further away from the Sun the general tendency is for the average density of the planet to decrease, but there are two exceptions for good reasons and this point is discussed in greater detail in Appendices 6, 7 and 8 where the formation of each planet and their moons is described in more detail.

Further Reading

Esposito L *The Changing Shape of Planetary Rings* Astronomy September 1987
Lewis J *The Chemistry of the Solar System* Scientific American September 1975
Kaufmann W J *Discovering the Universe* W H Freeman & Co New York 1990
Pollack J & Cuzzi J *Rings in the Solar System* Scientific American November 1981

CHAPTER SIX

CONSTRUCTION OF THE EARTH

'He made the earth by his power: he founded the world by his wisdom' (Jer. 51:15)

The Layered Earth

The Earth and its binary companion the Moon are both bodies that we have a great deal of knowledge of and the purpose of this chapter is to explain how the Earth was formed. The formation of the Moon is described in the next chapter.

Many Earth scientists incorrectly believe that when the Earth was first formed it was in a hot molten state with everything mixed up in a homogeneous state. This they say allowed the heavier material to sink down towards the core and the lighter material to rise up towards the surface. In this way over a period of thousands of millions of years the Earth became divided into a number of layers. This scenario seems reasonable enough, except that on closer scrutiny there are problems with it. For example it is difficult to see why such large continents should have formed and why these continents, being made of heavier material than water, are above sea level instead of being completely submerged under several hundreds of metres of salt water.

According to the theory that is proposed in this book the Earth was never in a molten state but was formed layer by layer from material in the Planetary Disc and was built up in conditions of extreme cold. Hence a detailed explanation for why the Earth has so many different layers has to be given. We also give a logical explanation for the formation of the continents which other theories do not give. The continents may be regarded as a late and final addition to our planet and more about this later.

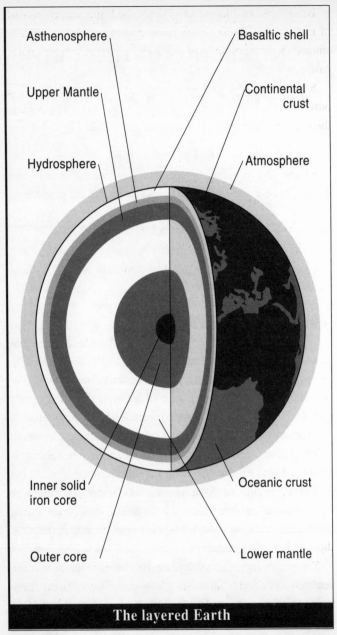

Asthenosphere

Basaltic shell

Upper Mantle

Continental crust

Hydrosphere

Atmosphere

Inner solid iron core

Oceanic crust

Outer core

Lower mantle

The layered Earth

Fig. 6.1

Before the continents were formed the Earth was composed of eight layers. These layers have only changed very slightly since they were formed and we can identify these layers fairly easily today.

Starting from the core at the centre of the Earth and working outwards the eight layers are as follows with the average thickness of each layer shown in brackets. (See Fig. 6.1.)

Inner Core........... (2740 km) (diameter)

Outer Core.......... (2100 km)

Lower Mantle..... (2200 km)

Upper Mantle...... (550 km)

Asthenosphere .... (150 km)

Basaltic Shell...... (6 km)

Hydrosphere .... (2.8 km)

Atmosphere .... (15+ km)

To these eight we can add one more layer called Continental Crust but as this layer is a late addition and is only found on 29% of the Earths surface it should not really be considered to be a layer in the same sense as the other layers which are truly global. The formation of the Continental Crust is explained in the next chapter.

That there are eight layers that make up our planet is something that we can be reasonably sure about.

The top layer - the Atmosphere - is something that we can feel and touch and breathe and fly through. It is made up mainly of the gases nitrogen and oxygen with a small amount of carbon dioxide and water vapour.

The next layer called the Hydrosphere consists of the oceans, seas and lakes of the Earth. There is so much water on the Earth that if this layer was uniformly thick it would make one global ocean with an average depth of over 2800m and there would be

75

no land anywhere. This was the situation at one point in time and the reason why this is not the case now is because of a stupendous event that took place not so long ago, which is described in the next chapter.

The Hydrosphere is also a layer that we know a great deal about.

The Continental Crust is the 'layer' upon which we build our homes and cities, grow our crops and obtain all the materials we need to sustain life. We have more knowledge of this layer than the others that lie below it. But we do not really know enough about this layer because we have only managed to drill a few kilometres into it and because of its great thickness and complexity we cannot say that we have thoroughly explored this layer.

Of the remaining six layers we know even less about, and what information we do have is largely based on detailed studies and analysis of the speed and type of seismic waves produced by earthquakes. Various types of waves travel through the Earth after an earthquake and these waves can be picked up by the hundreds of seismometers throughout the rest of the world. From the magnitude and timing of these readings it is possible to determine the velocity of these waves through the various layers that the waves must have passed through. This information can then be used in calculations to tell us something about the thickness and average density of each of these six layers but how accurate these estimations are is difficult to say.

It would be true to say that we have really only scratched at the surface of our planet and the Earth's interior has not yet been explored by man. Although the evidence that the Earth below the ocean bed is made up of six different layers is indirect, it is fairly convincing, but we have little information as to what precisely these layers are really composed of.

Another unknown quantity about the various layers is their temperature. From the very shallow boreholes and deep coal and diamond mines in the Continental Crust we know by measurement that in this layer only the temperature increases very rapidly with depth.

There is a popular but probably erroneous belief that this temperature variation in the top one or two kilometres below the surface continues all the way down some 6400km to the centre of the Earth so the deeper we go the greater is the temperature. If this was true the temperature of the centre of the Earth should be thousands of degrees and we should therefore have a liquid core but this is not consistent with the analysis of earthquake waves which indicate that the core is a solid body.

If however the theory for the formation of the planets from material in the Planetary Disc is correct then we have a basis for suggesting what each of these six layers are made from and this is described in this chapter.

All planets were formed layer by layer and this is true of the Earth as well. If we consider carefully the various steps from the first to the last layer of the Earth, the conclusion that we would have to come to is that the temperature in the lower parts of the Continental Crust should indeed be expected to be very high but the temperature in the Core should still be well below freezing and this would be consistent with the analysis of earthquake waves and the Earth's magnetism.

The low temperature of Jupiter's Red Spot (which we have suggested in Appendix 7 is the remains of an iron core) lends support to the idea that the iron core of all planets including ours is also still very cold as it was formed in freezing conditions and was well insulated afterwards.

In this chapter we explain how the Earth got its eight layers starting with the core and working upwards to the Basaltic shell, the oceans and finally the atmosphere.

We will not explain in this chapter the formation of the all important Continental Crust, which is not really a layer at all, and came into existence much later in a sudden and very dramatic manner - an event which merits the whole of the next two chapters.

Inner Core

'Where were you when I laid the earth's foundation?
Tell me if you understand.' (Job 38:4)

The Earth began its existence as a small ball, no bigger than a mustard seed, made from iron or nickel which was scattered as dust throughout the inner and outer regions of the Planetary Disc and which then became concentrated in rings.

The small iron seed was magnetic and grew by attracting other particles of magnetic material and thus increased in mass continually by sweeping up all magnetic material in its spiral path through the Planetary Disc (see Figure 5.3). From a seed it grew into a ball and from this into a bigger ball and so on.

When the ball of iron became too heavy for it to remain in a particular orbit it simply moved inwards in the Planetary Disc and thus found itself in a richer field of iron and so on like a snowball it grew rapidly as it spun its way through the rings attracting all the iron it could and rotating slowly as it did so to trap all the angular momentum of the captured iron particles. A good proportion of frozen hydrogen helium and ices of various kinds was also incorporated into the core at the same time as these materials were very abundant and present throughout the Planetary Disc.

Eventually the ball became a gigantic one and grew to a size in excess of 5000km in diameter. Thus the cold solid rotating core of the Earth was formed and this core became the foundation for the building of the rest of the planet.

The Earth's core is about the size of our Moon but being made mainly of iron, it weighs three or four times as much. When it reached its final size its orbit was still much further out in the Planetary Disc than the present orbit of the Earth.

The temperature of the core was extremely low - somewhere in the region of 200 degrees below freezing as by this time the whole of the Planetary Disc had radiated away most of its heat and there was no other source of heat. The core was also formed sufficiently slowly to allow any heat generated by impact and compression to be radiated away.

The formation of the iron Inner Core was the first stage in the construction of the Earth.

Outer Core

The Inner Iron Core was very heavy and therefore powerful enough to attract by its own gravity all readily available material in its continuing inward spiralling path through the Planetary Disc.

Among the other elements created in great abundance in the collapse of the Binary Sun were oxygen and carbon and hydrogen. These elements were able to combine to form water and a huge range of hydrocarbons. Thus in virtually all the rings where the temperature was low enough huge quantities of water ice particles and frozen hydrocarbons were formed and concentrated in rings. In the intense cold some of this material had aggregated into solids the size of pebbles boulders and larger asteroids.

The very heavy iron Core thus found itself spiralling through rings of ice asteroids and it no longer had to depend on its magnetism and the availability of iron to grow in size. Its own gravity was now sufficient to attract whatever material it could. Thus gases of various kinds present in the rings easily condensed and solidified on the Core by virtue of the very low temperature. Thus very quickly the cold Core became covered with layer upon layer of rock hard ices of all kinds.

This process went on for some time and resulted in the formation of a thick shell of ice and frozen hydrocarbons round the iron Core. The thickness of this shell is thought to have been at least 1900km and this layer has now been identified as the Outer Core. Its formation completed the second stage in the Earth's construction.

Lower Mantle

The increase in mass of the growing Earth, following its acquisition of its Outer Core of ice and frozen hydrocarbons was large enough to enable it to continue its spiralling journey away from the intensely cold regions rich with gases of all kinds towards the very slightly warmer regions containing less particles of ice but much more particles of fine dust made from rock minerals of all kinds. Many of these particles had by this time already aggregated into boulders and small asteroids of a large variety of rock minerals. Thus, as the ever growing Earth continued to spiral its way through very dusty regions, it came under intensive bombardment by dust, asteroids of rock minerals and asteroids of ice. The first few billion asteroid encounters were not particularly violent as the masses involved were not very large.

Continual and rapid accretion of the dust and asteroids resulted in the formation of another layer some 1700km thick, which completely covered up the Outer Core. This layer has been recognised as the Lower Mantle and is a mixture of rock minerals, water and other fluids of different kinds all of which make it a semisolid.

The accretion of the rocky material resulted in the young Earth growing into an even larger body. In the very early stages this body looked not unlike a huge construction site with untidy heaps of rubble from broken up asteroids piled up on top of each other with clouds of dust and thousands of frozen lakes and ponds.

By this time the young Earth rotated round its axis quite rapidly as all the angular momentum of the material it had collected was now locked into it. Hence gravitational and centrifugal forces took control, settled the dust and tidied up the heap into a near spherical shape with an ice covered surface cratered only by late arrival asteroids.

With the formation of the Lower Mantle the Earth attained about 80% of its final size.

Upper Mantle

With the completion of the Lower Mantle the partially completed Earth next moved even further inwards into the Planetary Disc and now encountered some of dust and asteroids made from heavier rock minerals in the Disc. The amount of water and gases in this region was still quite high. Billions of asteroid collisions and acquisition of thick layers of dust increased the diameter of the Earth by a further few hundred kilometres. These collisions were significantly more violent as the mass of the Earth was now very high, and the size and mass of the asteroids was also very high. In this way another layer some 500km thick was formed which today we recognise as the Upper Mantle. This layer is similar in physical properties to the Lower Mantle but contained less lighter fluids and a greater proportion of heavier rock minerals.

The Basaltic Shell

The completion of the Upper Mantle further increased the mass of the nearly completed Earth so it was able to continue to move even further inwards into the Planetary Disc. It now encountered the very heavy rock minerals of this region of the

Disc. As the gravitational attraction of the Earth was still very high asteroids made up of heavy rock minerals rained down violently on the surface of the Upper Mantle and the heat generated by the continual bombardment of these asteroids was sufficient to cause widespread melting or vaporisation of the asteroids and also of the surface of the Upper Mantle. The asteroid bombardment continued relentlessly until the supply of dust and asteroids in the rings of the Planetary Disc in this region was almost exhausted.

The effect of steady and usually violent asteroid impacts resulted in the melting of the basaltic asteroids and dust which quickly spread as molten rock and became solidified on cooling.

In this way the surface of the Upper Mantle became covered in layer upon layer of a heavy basaltic rock. For a short while after the asteroid bombardment had ceased numerous volcanoes developed in the fragile basaltic layer and these had the effect of pouring out billions of tonnes of molten basaltic rock over the previously cooled rock. Each stray asteroid collision generated much heat and the result of this heat was the melting of the previously deposited basaltic rock, and thus huge seas of molten basalt-exactly like the mares on the Moon - were formed at different times over the entire planet. The molten basalt flowed, but cooled very rapidly as modern flows of basaltic lava do, and hardened quickly at the surface.

In this way the young Earth obtained a shell of basaltic rock which neatly enclosed all the material that the Earth had gathered up on its long journey from the outer regions of the Planetary Disc to more or less where it is today.

This shell took Earth Scientists a little while to identify because it is now only accessible at the bottom of the oceans under a very thick deposit of sediments, the origin of which is explained in the next chapter.

The thickness of this shell today is very variable, as can be expected, but on average it is only five or six kilometres thick now. Like a crust on a cooling liquid which gradually thickens with time the basaltic shell was no more than a few hundred metres thick at first but became thicker all the time.

Although several kilometres thick now, the basaltic shell may be regarded as flexible and not unlike in behaviour to the skin of a football. It is capable of moving up or down in response to pressures from below. It is also able to move upwards slightly when tugged by the Sun and Moon's gravity or the gravity of a massive comet that passes in close proximity.

It is on this shell that the Continental Crust was formed and for this reason the shell may be regarded as the foundation of the continents.

In view of all the loads imposed upon it and its relatively small thickness it has become severely cracked into a dozen or so slabs called plates, and the study of these plates has become a special branch of science called plate tectonics.

'all the foundations of the earth are out of course'

(Ps. 82:5)

With the formation of the Basaltic Shell the Earth had gained almost all the material it required to complete its task of becoming the most beautiful planet in the Solar System.

After the Earth obtained its basaltic shell its appearance was almost exactly how the Moon or the planet Mercury looks like today - barren and pock marked by craters and mares of once molten basalt. At this stage there was very little by way of atmosphere. Apart from a few small frozen lakes there was no water. The Earth got its oceans and atmosphere a little later.

The Asthenosphere

The Basaltic Shell was formed on top of the Upper Mantle as described above. But the Upper Mantle was not really suitable material upon which to found the Basaltic Shell.

This was because all previously formed layers were not thoroughly compacted because of the relatively low approach velocities and masses of accreting dust and asteroids.

Hence after formation of the Basaltic Shell all the previously formed layers were protected by the shell. Further asteroid impacts on the basaltic shell had the effect of causing shock waves and vibrations throughout the Earth and under these the contents of the Earth below the shell were able to shake down and compact just a little under their own weight. The very high liquid and water content allowed some of the trapped lighter material to rise and the heavier trapped material to sink.

This adjustment of all the previous layers resulted in the formation of another layer only about 150km thick which developed immediately under the Basaltic Shell gradually as expected. This very important layer has now been recognised and is today called the Asthenosphere.

The Asthenosphere was, and still is, composed of gases, water, oils and other liquids including molten rock. This mobile and very hot material could not travel above the basaltic shell because by this time the shell had thickened sufficiently to prevent this from happening.

The Asthenosphere is a layer that is constantly growing in thickness and now contains not only extremely hot water and gases of various kinds but also minerals of many kinds formed by physical and chemical processes in an environment of heat, fluctuating pressure and abundant fluids. See Fig 6.2.

If one day we are able to explore this layer we should not be surprised to find that the material in this layer has arranged itself according to density with the lightest elements hydrogen

84

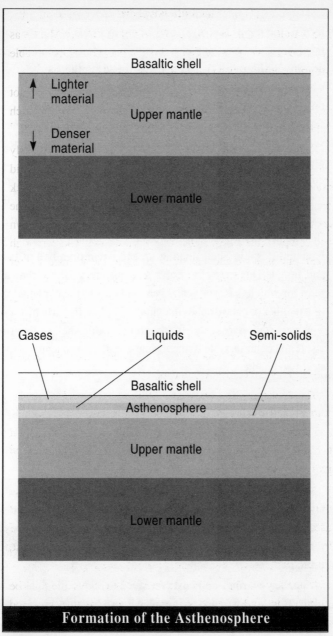

Formation of the Asthenosphere

Fig. 6.2

85

and helium in great quantities lying in a highly compressed form at the top of this layer, and heavy minerals at the base of this layer and everything else in between layered according to density. Almost all the oil and gas found on the Earth today was originally formed in the Planetary Disc. This was gathered up by the inner core and lay trapped deep below the Earth's surface by the Basaltic Shell. Some of this gas and oil has since seeped upwards and through weaknesses in the Basaltic Shell and become trapped again in the rock and sediments of the continental crust. It is these trapped hydrocarbons that are today exploited for fuel.

While the Basaltic Shell may be regarded as a fairly solid but flexible layer, the Asthenosphere is a soft 'springy' layer so we have the Basaltic Shell floating up and down on a bed of gas and liquid. This gives the Earth a 'bounciness', the technical term for which is isostasy, and is a vital clue to the explanation of a number of catastrophes that hit the Earth in its early history. This very important feature of the solid basaltic shell resting on a soft and compressible Asthenosphere is discussed again in the next two chapters.

The Hydrosphere

'Who shut up the sea behind doors when it burst forth from the womb..' (Job 38:8)

Once the Earth had gathered most of the material that it could from the final rings of dust and asteroids that it had to pass through, it became locked at last in an orbit close to its present orbit.

Smaller asteroids and dust continued to add to the thickness of the Basaltic Shell and as it cooled it also became thicker and stronger.

Meanwhile vast quantities of gas and hot salted water had begun to accumulate just below the shell in the Asthenosphere. Very little of this material could escape to above the hard shell because of its great thickness and strength.

This might have been the final stage and fate of our planet and in this case the Earth would simply look like a bigger version of the Moon or the planet Mercury. But Nature would not have it so.

Not very far from the young and barren Earth another baby planet with a core and covering of ice asteroids and dust also formed in much the same way as the Earth, and at the same time as the Earth, but in a region of the Planetary Disc only a little way further out. On completion this baby planet was about 1100km in diameter. We will use the name Pangaea for this very important baby planet and the choice for this name is explained in the next chapter.

The Earth and baby planet Pangaea enjoyed quite independent orbits round the dormant Sun for some time but as both bodies were still increasing in mass as a result of continued accretion of material from the Planetary Disc, the orbits of both bodies became gradually smaller as they both continued to spiral inwards towards the dormant Sun.

With spiralling orbits it was inevitable that a time would come when both bodies would come close to each other for the two bodies to join up. This is what did happen and baby planet was captured by the freshly formed Earth to form a close unbalanced binary system in exactly the same way as the Earth today endures the company of the Moon in a balanced binary system.

Being unbalanced the gravitational interaction between the young Earth and baby Pangaea increased uncomfortably as now Pangaea was obliged to spiral in towards the Earth and rotate around the Earth. With each revolution it tugged at the still fragile Basaltic shell of the Earth.

The tug on the Earth from Pangaea proved to be too great for the thin and freshly formed Basaltic Shell of the Earth which at this time also had huge quantities of hot highly pressurised liquid immediately under it.

Pangaea came much too close and the Basaltic Shell responded like it does today to the gravitational pull of the Moon. The shell rose up and allowed huge cracks to develop.

This was the moment that the trapped material below the shell was waiting for. When the shell cracked like an egg, billions of cubic metres of very hot salted water gushed out of these cracks and completely covered the Earth to a depth of over 2000m within a very short period of time. Most, but not all of the trapped water managed to escape. Under the weight of the water the shell sank downwards again and thus sealed itself. Molten basaltic rock also oozed out again in a desperate effort to cover over the cracks and strengthen the shell.

The escaped water formed a global ocean of warm salty water and immense clouds of water vapour also enveloped the still darkened Earth.

> *'.. the sea...when I made the clouds its garment and wrapped it in thick darkness'* (Job 38:9)

Thus the Earth got its Hydrosphere - not by the slow accumulation, over millions of years, of water condensed from the vapour emitted by volcanoes as is popularly believed, but in a matter of days or hours by the dramatic splitting up of the Basaltic Shell that contained it until just the right time for its release.

The Atmosphere
Many Earth scientists believe that the Earth was formed in what is called a reducing atmosphere (which is simply an atmosphere

rich in hydrogen and poor in oxygen) and gained its present oxygen and nitrogen rich atmosphere later on. Hitherto the reasons for this change in atmosphere has not been fully understood but if we continue to think of oxygen and nitrogen like any other material in the Planetary Disc, the reason why the Earth was formed in a hydrogen atmosphere which was later replaced by its present atmosphere becomes quite clear.

As hydrogen was abundantly present throughout the Planetary Disc it is not surprising that there is so much evidence in the rocks of the earth for an earlier hydrogen atmosphere.

After the Earth gained its hydrosphere its atmosphere was almost entirely water vapour in its lower parts and hydrogen and helium in the uppermost parts.

Other gases like nitrogen may also have been released into the atmosphere at the same time but the most probable source of oxygen and nitrogen was again the Planetary Disc. The outer regions of the Disc contained these gases in layers and rings as with other material. Some time after all the planets had formed the gases of the outer rings continued to contract. It is fortunate for us that the watery Earth found itself in orbit within a ring that was first very rich in oxygen and then very rich in nitrogen because oxygen is only a little heavier than nitrogen and the two gases followed each other in the Disc. The Earth was thus able to claim these gases from the rings simply by orbiting in them and allowing its own gravity to do the work. The Earth might have been swamped by other light gases like ammonia, methane, hydrogen and helium but thankfully for us these gases were first claimed by Venus, Jupiter and the other planets before they got as far as the Earth's orbit.

With the acquisition of its atmosphere the Earth now was almost completed - but it was just a warm watery desert with no land anywhere and in total darkness, as the dormant sun at this stage had not yet begun to shine.

And the Earth was still troubled by baby planet Pangaea, which was now in an unsteady orbit round the Earth and continued to trouble the Earth by raising immense tidal waves on the warm salty global ocean.

In this chapter we have described how the Earth got its eight layers. In the next chapter we describe how the Earth got the layer that is most important to us - the land upon which we live on.

Further Reading
Bolt B A *The Fine Structure of the Earth's Interior* Scientific American March 1973
Gass I G, Smith P J & Wilson R C *Understanding the Earth* Cambridge M.I.T. Press 1971
Press F & Siever R *Earth* (Second Edition) W H Freeman & Co San Francisco 1977
Morrison D *Asteroids* Astronomy June 1976

CHAPTER SEVEN

THE SUBMERGED
SUPERCONTINENT

Laurasia and Gondwanaland

The previous chapter explained how after the fracture of its fragile basaltic shell the young Earth became completely engulfed in a very deep ocean of warm salty water and there was no dry land anywhere. In this chapter we explain how the Earth very suddenly acquired a huge landmass in the form of a near circular supercontinent.

The Earth would have remained a watery or icy desert for ever - apart possibly for a few small islands which would really be the tops of sea bed volcanoes such as the Canary Islands in the Atlantic or the Hawaiian Islands in the Pacific - had it not been for a very dramatic event.

Today the Earth has the separated continents of North and South America, Australia, Antarctica and Africa all situated at great distance from the main land mass of Eurasia. But only less than five thousand years ago all these continents were not separated out but joined up into just one extensive supercontinent called Pangaea (all lands) made up of two parts called Laurasia and Gondwanaland.

Any story of the Earth's creation is not complete without an explanation as to how this supercontinent was formed and how why and when it subsequently split up into the six continents that we have on the Earth today.

The explanation given in this chapter is consistent with the theory for the formation of the Earth that we have so far described in this book.

Most Earth scientists now accept that all the present continents were indeed joined up into one giant supercontinent and have used the name Pangaea for it. When this was first suggested about four hundred years ago it was almost completely ignored. When the theory was again proposed some ninety years ago it was greeted with a great deal of scepticism and much derision. But as our knowledge of the geology of the ocean floor and each continent has increased vastly the theory that the continents have drifted apart from each other has gained acceptance and only within the last forty years has the idea of continental drift become regarded almost as a proven fact.

There is however no consensus of opinion as to how the giant supercontinent was formed and (until now) this is still something of a mystery. Because of this there is also some uncertainty about how, why and when the supercontinent split up.

Many Earth scientists believe that the supercontinent split up because the base upon which it was formed split up into plates which then moved apart from each other carrying with them parts of the supercontinent. Each plate is thought to act like a raft floating on the near molten Asthenosphere. In this case movement only becomes possible if the leading edge of one plate dives under another plate like one raft crashing into another and going under it. When this happens, some scientists think, a strip of Asthenosphere becomes exposed along the trailing edge of the plate and molten rock comes to the surface and cools rapidly to form a new fresh strip of ocean floor running parallel to the trailing edge of the plate. All this is said to happen at only a few millimetres per year.

The power for this movement of the plates is thought to be convectional currents in the Asthenosphere. This can be demonstrated in a pan of milk on a hotplate. The thin skin of cream formed at the surface of the warm milk will stay in place until the milk boils when convectional currents in the hot milk may be sufficient to split up the skin and drag it to one side and then down to the sides of the pan. This is the basis of the theory popularly used to explain why continents drift apart. But not all scientists agree with this theory.

There is another much simpler theory to explain why when and how the continents split up and again this theory is in keeping with the rest of this book and is proposed in this chapter.

While the origin of the supercontinent remains something of an unsolved mystery for many scientists, the interpretation of just about every physical feature on the Earth is also difficult. But once the origin of the supercontinent is understood its physical features are easily explained.

For example, at present the most favoured theory for the origin of the continents is that they are made of lighter material and simply floated to the top like froth in a boiling pot. But if this was the case we would expect to find not one near circular supercontinent on just one side of the globe but millions of small islands uniformly distributed throughout the Earth instead. Yet an examination of the globe shows even now that more than 70% of the Earth's surface has no land at all and that almost all of the land that we do have lies on one side of the globe only so we may rightly ask why this should be so.

If it was simply a matter of the lighter material floating to the top then water should be above everything because this is the lightest material available in abundance on the Earth and there is enough of it in the oceans to cover the whole Earth to a depth of at least two thousand metres.

Moreover for lighter material to float to the top would require the Earth to be in a molten, mobile state and there is no reason why it should ever have been so. In any case there is still a vast amount of heavy material within the land masses (for example iron ore) which according to the popular theory should have sunk down if the Earth was in a molten state. For all these reasons we have to dismiss the currently accepted theory that the supercontinent was formed by flotation as unsatisfactory and unscientific and another theory is therefore required.

Assembled in space

Earth scientists have got a rather poor idea of what is really going on in the depths of the Earth and for this reason have failed to come up with a viable theory for the origin of the supercontinent. But even if they did know more about the depths below, they would still have not solved the mystery of the origin of the supercontinent because the answer to this age old problem is not to be found in the depths below but in the heavens above.

To understand how the supercontinent was formed we need to focus our attention on the baby planet Pangaea once again. In the last chapter we saw how this very large baby planet was instrumental in breaking open the Earth's thin basaltic shell and releasing water from the Earths interior to form the warm global ocean.

It would be easy to think that Pangaea had the intelligence to prepare the Earth for a soft landing by itself and deliberately caused the release of water from below the Earth's basaltic shell.

Pangaea began its existence like all other miniplanets with a small core of magnetic material somewhere near the present orbit of Mars. It was formed layer by layer at a time when the Planetary Disc was still dense with dust and gas particles that had been sorted out into rings. The small iron core of Pangaea soon became covered over with material as it spiralled its way inwards through the Disc beginning with light weight material and collecting progressively heavier material as it moved inwards in the Disc. The iron core first picked up quantities of water and hydrocarbon ices of every description which settled on its core and this formed a thick shell of ice round the core. Vast quantities of pure carbon dust was also gathered up by this baby planet.

As the core with its thick covering of ice moved further inwards in the Planetary Disc it became covered over with dust and asteroids made up from lighter granitic rock minerals. It also gathered up material from rings which had become rich with minerals containing metals like iron, tin, copper, aluminium, silver and gold.

In the last stage of its inward journey through the Planetary Disc it received a coating of even heavier rock minerals including radioactive elements like Uranium.

Finally it too developed a basaltic shell. Nature, it seems, wanted to ensure that all the precious contents inside Pangaea was protected by a shell like an egg or inside a basket..

'Who has held the dust of the earth in a basket' (Isa. 40:12)

At this stage Pangaea looked just like the planet Mercury or the Moon but it was only about 1100km in diameter.

The orbits of the young Earth and the Pangaea were however dangerously near to each other and Pangaea soon succumbed into the clutches of the Earth's gravity. For a while it began to revolve round the Earth as a very close binary system.

The first effect of this capture was the fracture of the Earth's Basaltic shell, which resulted in the release of hot salty water from under the Earth's basaltic shell and the sudden formation of the Earth's oceans as described in the previous chapter.

Pangaea, having now been captured by the Earth, continued to orbit round our planet in much the same way as our Moon does churning up huge high tidal waves in the global ocean as it did so. With each revolution there was a transfer of energy. The basaltic shells of both the Earth and Pangaea were raised and allowed to drop at least once a day on every part of both components of this close binary, so that there was an immense transfer of energy which was absorbed by each component. This meant that both components of the binary began to experience a heating up of their material under their basaltic shells.

Founded first and established later

'The earth is the Lord's... for he founded it upon the seas and established it upon the waters' (Ps. 24:1)

The waters of the Earth's freshly released global ocean were warm and prevented from freezing by the thick very warm atmosphere.

The Earth/Pangaea binary system was not a stable one and like many binaries it served its purpose and then eventually collapsed.

The collapse was literally an Earth shattering event. A proper understanding of this collapse is essential if we are to understand how the supercontinent was formed, how it came to have the rich variety of soils, rocks and minerals, how it broke up, and how this breaking up led to the formation of chains of high mountains and other physical features.

As with all binary collapses the collision was not a head on one. In other words Pangaea did not fall on to the Earth vertically from the sky. If it had the Earth would have been a very different place with possibly just one not very large continent.

A binary system collapses by the smaller body spiralling into the larger body so that just before impact Pangaea travelled almost horizontally just above the surface of the Earth's global ocean at a velocity in excess of hundreds of metres per second causing tremendous disturbances in the atmosphere as well as in the waters of the ocean.

Pangaea encircled the young Earth several times at high speed at a level of only a few hundred kilometres to begin with but this height reduced with each revolution. Its speed also increased even more with each revolution as it retained its angular momentum until the very last second.

Finally the mutual gravitation between Pangaea and the Earth became too great and Pangaea came low enough to touch the waters of the Earth like an enormous spaceship. It skimmed for a very short time along the surface of the global ocean and in the next instant hit the ocean bed hard.

Amazingly the toughness of the Earth's basaltic shell withstood the first impact. The impact was cushioned to a small extent by the deep ocean and the flexibility of the basaltic shell and like a rubber ball Pangaea almost immediately bounced off again.

This first Pangaea/Earth kiss may have only taken a second or two but that was all that was required to have three very important effects.

Firstly it cracked and weakened the Earth's basaltic shell in the area where the impact took place causing a huge depression several thousand kilometres in diameter radiating from under the centre of the impact.

Secondly a small but very significant volume of the soft and liquid Asthenosphere under the basaltic shell was squeezed outwards radially, resulting in a slight but extremely significant uplift of the shell around the rim of the depression. See Fig. 7.1.

A simple experiment to understand this can easily be done. Take two ordinary rubber spherical balloons of different size. Blow them up with water rather than air. Next hit the larger one with the smaller and note the deformation pattern on the larger.

The circular uplift of the basaltic shell on the rim of the depression is of great significance. Without this, as we will see later, the continents of North and South America and Australia would not have been stopped in their tracks and would have slid all the way to inside this depression and become totally submerged under the waters of the Pacific ocean.

Thirdly the first impact of Pangaea on the Earth also severely damaged the baby planet itself, shattering its fragile basaltic shell and allowing some of its contents to burst out and fall into the global ocean.

The severely damaged, but not yet completely broken, Pangaea rose a few thousand metres again out of the water and continued its doomed flight for a minute or two more. During this very short time Pangaea, which still had a rotation about its own axis, now did not have the necessary velocity to escape the full influence of the very strong gravitational attraction of the Earth.

Finally Pangaea hit the ocean again on the other side of the globe and this time it did not have the restitution to bounce off and thus almost came to rest on the Earth's basaltic shell. The impact did not however entirely stop the rotation of Pangaea that it had about its own axis, which it had acquired in space during its formation.

Consequently Pangaea continued to rotate in the area it found itself in and thus ground itself to a halt. In doing so it became deeply embedded into the Earth's basaltic shell, scattering its contents and generating huge quantities of heat in the process.

The contents of the baby planet thus spread out over the basaltic shell like thick fluids from a broken egg.

'...who spread the earth upon the waters' (Ps. 136:6)

The Earth's basaltic shell responded to the extra weight im-

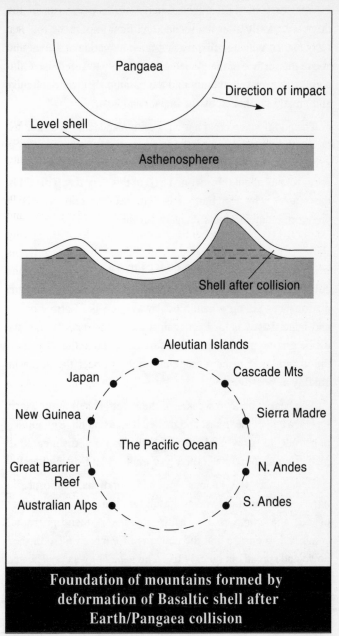

Foundation of mountains formed by
deformation of Basaltic shell after
Earth/Pangaea collision

Fig. 7.1

posed upon it by sinking further into the soft Asthenosphere, so that very shortly after the second and final impact the rotating baby planet, which at first stuck out for hundreds of kilometres above the surface of the global ocean, rapidly lowered itself like a gigantic overweight buoy into the basaltic shell now softened and greatly weakened by the impact and heat.

The additional weight and momentum suddenly acquired by the Earth through its capture of Pangaea was sufficient to tilt the axis of rotation of the Earth by twenty three degrees and the Earth rotates about this inclined axis to this very day. This tilt is the reason why the Earth has four seasons and we could therefore blame or thank Pangaea for this.

Pangaea under the sea

After the two impacts the resultant atmospheric and ground disturbances set up gigantic tidal waves on the Earth's ocean and huge waves lapped up against the remains of the rapidly disintegrating planetesimal that still stuck above the surface of the waters as if to help erode and hide it under the ocean as quickly as possible.

The heat generated weakened the basaltic shell upon which Pangaea had come to rest and melted it, causing huge quantities of basalt to flow and parts of the rapidly disintegrating planetesimal found itself on top of molten and flowing basalt.

Hence the tremendous ground vibrations, atmospheric winds, incessant tidal waves, basalt flows and, most important of all, the compressible nature of the Asthenosphere all combined to ensure that the contents of Pangaea were pushed down and spread out quickly like a huge ball of wax on a heated surface.

In time all of the crashed planetesimal was reduced to a gigantic mound made from molten material and thick fluids of sediments and boulders of all sizes spread over a near circular area that now stretched some 7000km in diameter.

The mound was reduced in level so much that in time it disappeared completely below the ocean waves and what was once a deep ocean in this part of the Earth now became a shallow sea over a submerged and very hot mound that marked the area where the baby planet Pangaea was buried.

From time to time in response to the great pressure from below parts of the gigantic mound rose above and fell below sea level and this movement allowed vast quantities of sediment to be transported from the ocean floor to the top and sides of the mound and back again to the ocean floor.

In this way many parts of the mound developed a layered system of soils and rocks.

While submerged in this way a large proportion of the sediments in the mound underwent some important changes.

The tremendous heat generated at the base of the mound was sufficient to change some of the sediments almost beyond recognition. Most of the rocks on our continents that we call metamorphic rocks were formed by this heat. Thus clays were baked to shales and claystone and sands cemented into sandstones and so on.

The process of deposition, consolidation and baking of the sediments went on for possibly hundreds of years and after this period the dust and sediments originally gathered by the baby planet Pangaea from the rings of the Planetary Disc changed into a highly complex system of igneous, metamorphic and sedimentary rocks as well as layers of soils such as sands and clays. The geology of all the continents of the Earth can be satisfactorily interpreted in terms of the changes that took place on the sediments of the crashed and broken baby planet while these were submerged under the ocean and heated from below at the same time. In this book it is not possible to explain in detail how all the clays and sands and rocks now found on the Earth were formed but all the conditions required for their formation were present in this submerged mound which was continuously heated from below.

The next momentous event that took place on the Earth was much later and this event was the raising of the now fully matured and geologically developed mound from below sea level to just high enough above sea level for the top of the mound to drain off and allow the dry land known as Supercontinent Pangaea to appear.

This event is linked to the formation and capture of the Moon which became the Earth's next binary partner shortly after the submerged mound and remains of Pangaea had matured and was ready to be raised up above sea level.

The Independent Moon

The Moon was formed separately like all other baby planets from the material in the Planetary Disc at about the same time as the Earth but a few million kilometres away and enjoyed its own orbit which was further out than its present orbit.

Being so near to us now the Moon is a body which we know quite a lot about. It is also a layered structure and the following layers starting from the centre are thought to exist.

Iron core	(600km in diameter)
Outer core	(400km thick)
Mantle	(1000km thick)
Basaltic shell	(60-150km thick)

The Iron Core was formed like all other iron cores in the outer part of the Planetary Disc. It grew in size to a diameter of 600km, by which time it had found its way into that part of the Planetary Disc which was rich in gases and dust made up from

102

some of the lighter minerals. It was able to pick these up and thus formed its semi liquid outer core, and in doing so grew to a size of about 1000km in diameter. It continued its journey through the dust and asteroids of the medium heavy minerals and thus obtained a very thick coating of these minerals, which now form its rigid Mantle. By this time it had grown to a sphere some 3400km in diameter and then found itself in the rings of the Planetary disc containing the heavy basaltic minerals. As a result of quite violent asteroid impacts, it was able to develop a basaltic shell of variable thickness and by this time the Moon had acquired all its material and became a sphere of 3476km in diameter. Its average density is, as expected, much lower than the Earth's average density, bearing in mind that its main constituent was formed from light rock minerals and it is likely that the Moon's iron core is surrounded by an outer core of ice. As the Moon's iron core also gathered up vast quantities of ice and hydrocarbons from the Planetary Disc there should be large quantities of water, oil and gas trapped below the Moon's basaltic shell. Being smaller than the Earth it is also not as well compacted, and partly for this reason the overall density of the Moon is much lower than that of the Earth.

The Moon was also able to gather up a few very heavy asteroids from the innermost rings of the Planetary Disc. Many of these heavy asteroids became embedded in the Moon's basaltic shell as what have come to be known as mascons which can today be detected under the surface of the Moon by their high gravity.

During its formation and for a short while afterwards the Moon enjoyed an independent existence in an orbit close to the Earth's but separate from it, and only a million or so kilometres further out.

A short time after the Earth had gathered up all its material including the baby planet Pangaea it was able to capture the

Moon. The event that triggered off the capture of the Moon by the Earth is described in the next chapter.

This capture of the Moon did not result in a collision between the Moon and the Earth, but fortunately for us led to the emergence of the submerged remains of Pangaea enabling it to become the dry land of Supercontinent Pangaea. These very dramatic events are explained in the next chapter.

Further Reading
Wilson J T *Continents Adrift and Continents Aground:Readings from Scientific American* W H Freeman & Co. San Francisco 1976
Press F & Siever R *Earth* (Second Edition) W H Freeman & Co San Francisco 1977
Velikovsky I *Worlds in Collision* Gollancz, London 1950

CHAPTER EIGHT

THE FIRST SIX DAYS

The First Day

In the previous chapter we described how a baby planet, called Pangaea, crashed on to the newly formed watery Earth, and formed a submerged supercontinent under the global ocean, so that the Earth at this time still remained a dark, lifeless planet, completely covered over by a great depth of water.

The global ocean and the atmosphere were still warm as a result of the immense heat generated by the Pangaea/Earth collapse and a thick fog covered the whole planet.

'Now the earth was formless and empty, darkness was over the surface of the deep'....{Gen.1:2}

Left in this state the warm water would have cooled down very rapidly and eventually the fog on the whole planet would have cleared and the Earth would have become just a huge ice covered ball not unlike some of the moons of Jupiter. But Nature would not have it so and had to do four things to ensure that our planet would become what it is today.

Firstly Nature had to clear the very dense fog that completely covered the whole Earth.

Secondly Nature had to get rid of surplus ocean water.

Thirdly Nature had to allow a huge area of land to rise above sea level.

Fourthly Nature had to ensure that the Sun would burst into heat and light from its dormant state.

All four objectives were accomplished by just one major event which is described in this chapter.

According to the Bible the Earth enjoyed its first day only some six thousand years ago. This marvellous day began, not in the usual way with a sunrise, but with the sudden appearance of an extremely bright light.

The source of this light has been the subject of conjecture for centuries and many explanations have been put forward. Non Bible believers would say that there was no such light as the Sun must have already been shining for millions of years before the Earth was formed. Some Bible believers think that the light was a supernatural one for which no explanation is either possible or necessary. Yet others think that the light was not real but purely allegorical.

In this chapter we explain that the light was real, was to be expected and consistent with the theory that has been proposed for the Solar System in this book.

To understand what this light was it is necessary to go right back to the time when the Planetary Cloud was formed after the collapse of the Binary Sun.

The outermost regions of the cloud contained only the lightest materials which was almost entirely hydrogen and helium. In the extremely low temperatures in this region these gases froze and contracted into asteroids which then aggregated to form a planetesimal and finally into a massive planet not unlike Jupiter or Saturn. There are still millions of such asteroids in the region and from time to time these come close enough to the Sun and we see them as comets. More about these asteroids later on in this book.

The giant planet that was thus formed was unable to settle into a stable orbit and found itself spiralling in towards the dormant Sun because of its steadily increasing mass as it gathered up some of the abundance of unclaimed hydrogen and helium.

It is logical to use the name Solar C for this enormous planet because in many respects it was similar to the two original components of the Binary Sun which we named Solar A and Solar B.

Some six thousand years ago this enormous planet, like a gigantic comet, invaded the space occupied by the inner planets which had by this time already settled into stable orbits. The consequences of this intrusion for most of the inner planets including the Earth was tremendous.

When Solar C, travelling now at an estimated two million kilometres per hour entered the final stage of its spiralling journey towards the dormant Sun it encountered fierce resistance from unclaimed gas and dust and further resistance from the Solar Wind emanating from the still dormant Sun.

As a result of this resistance the surface layers of Solar C became heated into incandescence in the same way and for the same reason that a comet heats and lights up as it approaches the Sun. Quite suddenly, Solar C became a huge and brilliant object with sufficient brightness and radiation to floodlight and warm up half the entire watery surface of the Earth. Thus on the first day the Earth had its first experience of being dark on one side and brilliantly lit up on the other side.

'...and he separated the light from the darkness.' {Gen.1.4}

The Second Day

Towards the end of the first day Solar C came close enough to the Earth so that its huge gravitational tug was felt very strongly by the Earth.

The tug was sufficient to drag the Earth out of its then orbit into its present one and in doing so had other effects on the Earth.

The first effect of this tug was that billions of tonnes of the Earth's ocean water was sucked out almost instantaneously. This was as if Solar C made a bid to claim the entire mass of the Earth but only succeeded in obtaining part of its outer covering of water.

Some of this stolen water went all the way and became part of Solar C but a large proportion of it escaped this fate and was left suspended hundreds of kilometres above the Earth's surface where it dispersed to form a much needed protective canopy right round the Earth. Much of the fog that covered one side of the Earth was also instantaneously lifted off by the same gravitational tug

'Let there be an expanse between the waters to separate water from water....made the expanse and separated the water under the expanse from the water above it.' {Gen.1:7}

The Third Day

The sudden and tremendous loss of water from the Earth upset the delicate balance of the Earth's basaltic shell but furthermore the gravitational tug from Solar C also had an effect on the shell.

As expected the most vulnerable area of the shell was in those parts which were not protected by the additional weight of the submerged supercontinent.

One very large unprotected area of the shell, now relieved of a huge weight of water and under the gravitational effect from Solar C rose upwards slowly in response to the two forces acting on it.

The immediate result of this initially quite small uplift of the basaltic shell was that the remaining ocean water in the affected regions was able to drain away from the affected area, thus reducing the downward pressure on the shell even further. This in turn allowed the upward pressure from the Asthenosphere to lift the shell up further, thus causing even more water to drain away. And so the process continued.

The rising of the shell continued until the strain became too much. Finally, a point was reached when the basaltic shell cracked open and deep and wide fissures several thousand kilometres in length developed in the shell.

These cracks allowed billions of tonnes of superheated steam and vaporised rock material and other fluids which were trapped under the shell to escape into the atmosphere.

After escape of all this material the pressure in the Asthenosphere was much reduced. The tug from Solar C also diminished as it raced away towards the dormant Sun.

The risen and cracked basaltic shell thus plunged downwards again like parts of a deflated ball. In this way a deep depression formed in the affected area of the basaltic shell.

This huge depression - deeper than the initial dent caused by Pangaea - rapidly filled up with water from the now tempestuous global ocean.

As water entered into the depression, the shell sank downwards even more under its newly acquired weight thus making the depression even deeper, and so on the process continued for some time.

Today this depression is deeper and bigger than any other in the world and we know it today as the Pacific Ocean. Most of the remains of the huge cracks can still be detected today in the ocean bed and we call them deep sea trenches and ocean ridges.

'Have you journeyed to the springs of the sea or walked
in the recesses of the deep?' (Job.38:16)

This massive movement of water into the depression meant that on the other side of the globe the weight of water over the still submerged supercontinent now steadily decreased.

With the decrease of weight in the area of the supercontinent the pressure from under the basaltic shell in this area was able to simultaneously push the supercontinent upwards. This caused even more water to flow away to fill the deepening depression in the Pacific Ocean. In this way in a matter of only a few hours the supercontinent rose up from under the sea into the warmth of the Earth's atmosphere. The shape of the supercontinent is shown in Fig. 8.1.

'Let water under the sky be gathered in one place, and let dry ground appear.' {Gen.1:9}

Hence only as a result of a gravitational tug from an extremely massive rogue planet, billions of tonnes of water was displaced and this, as we have seen, finally allowed the supercontinent to appear at last above sea level.

The Fourth Day

Meanwhile the extremely massive Solar C continued racing away towards the still darkened dormant Sun and circled the dormant Sun at great speed several times in rapidly decreasing circles until it plunged deep into it and became an integral part of it.

The immediate effect of this collision was as expected a tremendous generation of heat which quickly spread over the entire surface of the receiving body so that in a matter of only a few hours the dormant Sun was changed from its darkened state into the bright star as we see it today. A fuller description of the collision and the effect that Solar C still has on the Sun is described in Appendix 5.

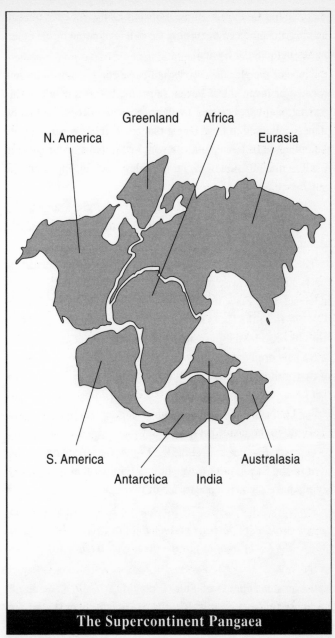

The Supercontinent Pangaea

Fig. 8.1

111

As would be expected the intrusion of the runaway planet also had the effect of disturbing the orbits of some of the other bodies in the Solar System.

Some of the planets already had close companions in binary systems or independent but close orbits, but as a result of the gravitational upset caused by the massive comet these binary planets collapsed to form single planets. A fuller description of the collapses of binary planets which may have occurred as a result of the intrusion of Solar C, is described in Appendices 6 and 7

Another extremely important effect of the giant comet was that the Earth was able to acquire its binary companion, the Moon.

The Moon was formed as a small and independent planet in much the same way that the Earth was formed but quite independently. For a while it enjoyed its own orbit just a little way out from the Earth's orbit. The Moon was also disturbed from its orbit by the intrusion of the rogue planet and dragged into a new orbit dangerously close to the Earth. In only a matter of two or three days the Earth was able to capture the Moon so that it was brought into the Earth's orbit. In doing so it was also obliged to become the Earth's binary partner and made to orbit the Earth in the manner it does today.

Once the Sun began to shine the Moon was able to reflect the light of the Sun. An observer on the Earth at that time would simply have seen the appearance of two lights.

'made two great lights-the greater light to govern the day and the lesser light to govern the night.' {Gen:1.16}

Left over small chunks of Solar C continued to fall on the Earth for some time afterwards. The Bible uses the word 'star' for meteorites as well as the planets. Hence the verse

Thus in a period of only a few days the Earth was transformed from a dark but warm watery planet to a place where there was now dry land and sea, and sunlight during the day and moonlight during the night.

With a thick layer of water vapour very high in the stratosphere the young Earth was protected from the strong Solar Wind which increased in intensity as a result the penetration of Solar C into the Sun.

The Fifth and Sixth Day

After the Sun began to shine conditions for the start and proliferation of life became absolutely ideal. The oceans and atmosphere were warm as a result of all the tremendous upheavals and release of superheated steam and other gases from below the basaltic shell.

Marine life in the ocean and bird life in the air and animal life on land began at last. This is considered in Appendix 9.

When it first emerged from under the ocean the supercontinent was in a very wet state, as may be expected with sea water in every tiny crack and void. For some centuries after it emerged from under the waves some of this water was changed by the immense heat into steam which made its way upwards to the surface and cooled down as water. For this reason numerous geysers and springs produced salt free water in great abundance which fed numerous rivers throughout the supercontinent.

The atmosphere was still far too warm for rain to fall but

> *'... streams (or mist) came up from the earth and watered the whole surface of the ground.' (Gen.2:6)*

Nature had at last accomplished its task of creating a planet upon which plant, animal and human life in great abundance could flourish.

Further Reading
Pimenta L R *Fountains of the Great Deep* New Wine Press Chichester 1984
Rosevear D *Creation Science* New Wine Press Chichester 1991
Sargeant D *Comets: Vagabonds of Space* Doubleday 1982
Velikovsky I *Worlds in Collision* Gollancz, London 1950

CHAPTER 9

THE PERIL OF THE MOON

Land and sea tides

The Earth's binary companion, the Moon, is an object of wonder and beauty in the night sky and it may even bring out the romance in us. But the truth is that it was and still is a dangerous partner for the Earth to have.

This is because the Moon has the ability to keep the Earth's Asthenosphere continually on the boil.

The reason for this is that the Moon is an unwilling partner that is tied to the Earth. It would really like to break free to resume its independent orbit that it once enjoyed.

As far as the Earth is concerned the Moon is like a heavy iron ball tied by a strong revolving chain to the Earth's basaltic shell.The 'chain' is in tension all the time year in and year out so that approximately once a day each part of the basaltic shell heaves upwards very slightly when the Moon is at its closest and sinks downwards again when the Moon has passed by.

The Moon exerts a gravitational pull on the whole Earth but the side facing the Moon feels the pull slightly more than the side away from the Moon. We watch the effect of this by the sea as the Moon raises and lowers the level of water on our oceans, and this leads to high and low tides on our coastlines. The amount of energy generated by the pull of the Moon (and Sun) can be gauged by just observing the tides.

But a lesser known fact is that the Moon (and Sun) also raises and lowers the Earth's basaltic shell and with it both land and sea levels are also affected. We can interpret these daily changes in level as responses due not only to the pull of the Moon, but also to the immense pressure from the Asthenosphere pushing the shell upwards. Over the centuries a state of balance has been achieved, so that the pull from the Moon and the push from below does not normally lead to catastrophic rises of the basaltic shell.

But the daily rise and fall in the basaltic shell results in a generation of heat in the Asthenosphere which results in a tiny but significant rise in temperature each day. The Asthenosphere is well insulated by the thick basaltic shell, so that the rate of generation of heat here is greater than the rate of loss of heat, which means that overall the temperature in the Asthenosphere is able to increase steadily each day. Over a period of several hundred years the temperature rise becomes very significant, as does the pressure.

When this temperature and pressure reaches a critical value the heat can be sufficient to partially melt and weaken the shell and the pressure is also able to lift up the basaltic shell.

Now if the shell is loaded by its own weight, together with the weight of a continent or deep ocean, then this downward load may be just sufficient to prevent the shell from rising upwards and cracking open.

If, however, there is a slight removal or reduction of the downward load on the shell then the precarious balance is lost and an upward rise of the shell causes the shell to burst open, resulting in a catastrophe of global proportions.

Hence all that is needed to cause a global catastrophe is a very slight reduction in the loading at the top of the shell and a passing comet or combined effects of the Sun with other planets is all that is necessary to upset the balance.

During the past six thousand years some major catastrophes of global proportions have been caused for this reason.

The first catastrophe caused a global flood that submerged the supercontinent into the ocean again for about a year.

A second catastrophe led to the breaking up of the super-continent into its eastern and western parts.

116

A third and fourth and possibly fifth catastrophe led to further breaking up of the eastern part of the supercontinent.

Earthquakes and violent volcanic eruptions may be regarded as modern day catastrophes that affect the Earth today on a smaller scale for the same reason.

The Great Flood

The first catastrophe is popularly known as Noah's Flood or the Great Deluge. While most people have heard or read about it, the magnitude and cause of this global disaster is not always appreciated. This terrible event wiped out almost the entire population of the world.

We know that it happened some sixteen centuries after the first day. A simple calculation shows that if there were only two people on the Earth to begin with, the population of the Earth would have risen to millions of people at the time of the flood so millions of people perished in the Great Flood.

The Earth was inhabited by races of highly intelligent people who kept records of important events that took place in the world at the time and these records are still preserved in the mythologies of people throughout the world.

The Great Flood was not the result of continuous rain only (as some believe) but as a result of upheavals in the Earth's basaltic shell which caused a sudden rise in sea level which in turn resulted in ocean waters flowing over the land masses.

Bearing in mind the manner in which the Earth obtained its thin basaltic shell and later on its supercontinent, a catastrophe causing the ocean waters to flow over the low lying land masses was almost predictable.

The cause of this catastrophe may again partly be attributed to the Moon. When captured by the Earth the Moon had an orbit round the Earth closer to its present orbit. We know this because the Moon today is receding from the Earth, and the of this is that it must have been closer to the Earth when first captured. A simple calculation based on the present recession rate shows that even only 4000 years ago the Moon was much closer to the Earth than it is at present.

During the early days after the Moon's capture the already hot material in the Asthenosphere under the Earth's basaltic shell was further heated with each daily rotation of the Earth. Continued compaction of material deep inside the Earth's interior also results in some heating up so it is not surprising that the basaltic shell which encloses everything is always in a precarious state of balance. It requires only a small additional force or weight reduction to upset this balance. And when this happens the consequences are catastrophic.

The description of the Great Flood given in the book of Genesis strongly suggests that the Flood was a natural and predictable event. It was a direct hit by an ordinary averaged size comet. Some 4400 years ago the Earth was hit by a comet which we will name Lamech after Noah's father. The reader is reminded that comets are asteroids made from dust and ices of all kinds which have not as yet found a resting place but continue to orbit the Sun in thousands of different orbits.

Comet Lamech was a fairly massive comet consisting of a fairly solid nucleus with a surrounding 'atmosphere' of dust and fine particles of ices of all kinds that stretched for thousands of kilometres from the nucleus.

Comet Lamech crashed into the Earth somewhere in the vast global ocean. The immediate effect of this was the generation of huge tidal waves in the global ocean which resulted in sudden and terrifying floods in all coastal regions

'And ....the floodwaters came on the earth.' (Gen.7.10)

Comet Lamech penetrated deep into the ocean and was powerful enough to depress a part of the Earth's basaltic crust and compact the Asthenosphere. This resulted in a sudden and tremendous increase in pressure of the Asthenosphere which in turn resulted in terrible earthquakes and uplift of vast tracts of land. Deep and wide tension cracks were thus formed throughout the Earth from which vast quantities of hot trapped gases, water and molten rock gushed out

'on that day all the springs of the great deep burst forth'
(Gen.7:11)

On that same fateful day the whole Earth suddenly found itself engulfed by the tail of the comet. Billions of tonnes of the comet's tail of dust and ices formed a blanket round the Earth that effectively blotted out the Sun so that suddenly the whole Earth was plunged into near complete darkness. All this would have taken the people living on the Earth by surprise. Only the previous day the weather throughout the Earth was bright, warm and dry just as it had been from the first day. But now the terrified inhabitants had to face massive earthquakes and tidal waves in near darkness.

The fine particles of frozen gases in the tail of Comet Lamech became integrated with the huge quantity of water vapour already in the Earth's warm atmosphere and with the vast quantity of water vapour generated by the tremendous heat of the ocean water in the collision area. The result of this was the almost instantaneous formation of an extremely thick and dark rain cloud that completely covered the land. The water vapour in this dark rain cloud was able to cool and condense rapidly to form large globules of water which fell as rain continuously for several weeks.

'and the floodgates of the heavens were opened. And rain fell
on the earth for forty days and forty nights' (Gen.7.11)

The basaltic shell making up the ocean floor also rose upwards by several hundred metres causing gigantic tidal waves and an immense rise in sea level throughout the world. As a result of this the ocean waters flowed over all the entire land mass and submerged it again drowning all of its hundreds of millions of inhabitants.

The supercontinent stayed completely submerged for five months

'The waters flooded the earth for a hundred and fifty days'
(Gen.7:24)

'The waters rose and covered the mountains to a depth of
more than twenty feet' (Gen.7:20)

Once again the Earth became a watery planet with no dry land anywhere. All land based life perished.

The supercontinent might have stayed submerged for ever, but all that was required to push the water away from the land back into the ocean was a wind.

The cause of this wind is easy to find. Warm water from the collision area made its way to the top of the ocean so that the air immediately above the ocean surface was also warmed up. In the area of the submerged supercontinent no such warming up was possible. This meant that the atmosphere above the submerged supercontinent was very slightly cooler than the atmosphere above the ocean. This enabled a 'land breeze' to develop with wind blowing from the colder waters covering the supercontinent towards the warmer waters of the deep ocean

The wind generated huge waves flowing away from the flooded supercontinent.

This gradual flow of water caused the ocean floor to subside as a result of the very slight increase in weight of water, and at the same time as the weight of water over the supercontinent decreased, the supercontinent began to rise. Such was the delicate balance in the basaltic shell.

Overall the effect was cumulative, and the water level over the supercontinent began to drain away rapidly once normal gravitational forces came into play. The faster the water drained away from the land areas the more the ocean bed adjusted to receive the waters and the more the supercontinent rose upwards in response to the loss in weight of water.

Once again dry land began to appear in much the same way as it did sixteen centuries earlier.

> *'..he sent a wind over the earth and the waters receded'*
> *(Gen.8:1)*

It took a good year from the time of the beginning of the Great Flood to its end when the supercontinent became dry land again.

After the Great Flood the world no longer enjoyed the benefits of a vapour canopy so that the full effect of the Earth's tilt could be felt for the first time

> *..seed time and harvest,*
> *cold and heat,*
> *summer and winter,*
> *day and night*
> *will never cease. (Gen.8:22)*

Life on the supercontinent resumed again, despite terrible and frequent earthquakes, as the supercontinent continued to be lifted up by the immense pressure under the basaltic shell for decades after all the flood water had gone.

Breakup of the Supercontinent

'One was named Peleg, because in his time the earth was divided' (Gen.10:25)

After the Great Flood life on the now nearly deserted super-continent resumed again for the next 120 years.

The very few survivors quickly increased in numbers again to a few thousand people, but some of these may have been affected by the next catastrophe which was the break up of the supercontinent Pangaea.

Just over a century after the Great Flood the supercontinent was divided into two parts, and to understand why this had to happen we need to consider the Asthenosphere of the Earth again.

During the Great Flood the temperature in the Asthenosphere under the supercontinent remained high but there was no breaking up of the Basaltic Shell because the weight of the supercontinent was able to contain the immense pressures from below.

The weight of the supercontinent itself allowed this part of the basaltic shell to withstand higher pressures than those parts of the shell without any such protection.

The huge temperature rise in the Asthenosphere caused by the impact of Comet Lamech also caused the basaltic rock at the base of the supercontinent to become very hot with virtually no strength.

Some 120 years later the base of the supercontinent became molten as a result of the immense heat that had built up. The now fluid rock at the base was able to flow with only the slightest provocation and carry with it parts of the super-continent itself as easily as raft of tied logs on a gently flowing river.

Gravity strives hard to keep the Earth spherical and any slight rise in level of the basaltic shell is sufficient to enable material in a fluid state to flow off from a higher level to a lower level.

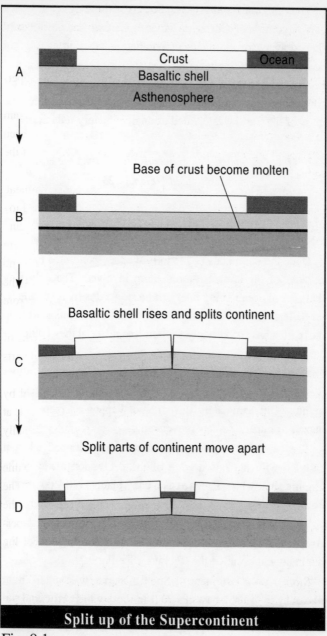

Split up of the Supercontinent

Fig. 9.1

123

Thus the continents now called North and South America parted company with what is now Europe and Africa and floated away for thousands of kilometres westwards on a thin bed of very hot molten rock. At the same time Africa and Europe moved eastward. As they moved, the newly broken off continents rotated a little as expected. And thus the single land mass of the Earth was divided as ancient history tells us.

'One was named Peleg, because in his time the earth was divided ' (Gen.10.25)

Man has only rediscovered this fact recently. Fig.9.1. illustrates this.

Once the continents began to move they continued to do so because of the immense momentum involved. The only way that a large ocean going liner can be stopped is by reversing its propellers, and in the same way once the continents started to move on a base of virtually friction free material they could not easily be stopped.

North and South America might have travelled much further westwards than they did in a period of only a few weeks or months. But fortunately this did not happen as there was a barrier to impede further movement.

The North American continent was only stopped when it collided with the raised edge of the depression made in the basaltic shell when Pangaea as a baby planet collided with the Earth.

The sudden stoppage of the moving continent of North America by this long obstruction led to the formation of the mountain chain called the Rockies. See Fig.9.2.

Similarly the continent of South America was halted in its tracks by the raised basaltic shell in the South Pacific and the Andean chain of mountains were formed virtually overnight.

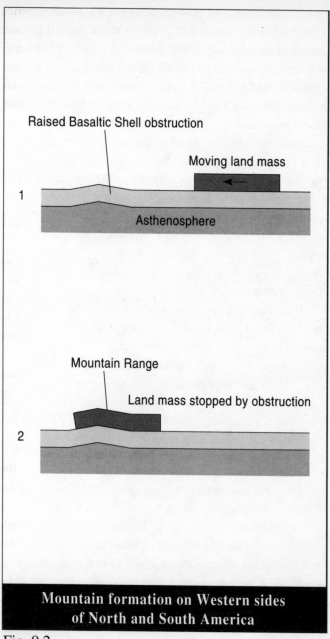

Mountain formation on Western sides
of North and South America

Fig. 9.2

When Africa moved eastward there was a lower obstruction to stop it but the eastern part of the continent appears to have gone over this obstruction which now lies under the highlands of Eastern Africa. This part of the Supercontinent is still moving eastward and has resulted in the formation of the Great Rift Valley which runs from Syria in the north to Mozambique in the south.

Some time later, for the same reason Antarctica also broke away from the supercontinent, but this continent had nothing to stop it and so slid all the way to the South Pole where it now is. Other movements of large land masses for the same reason caused a piece of land now known as India which was originally attached to Southern Africa to move northwards towards Asia and on colliding with another part of the Supercontinent, now called Asia, produced the Himalayan Range of mountains.

All the very high mountains of the world were created after the Great Flood when large tracts of moving land masses were brought to an abrupt halt as described above.

Before the break up there were some small mountains and hills, but as the Supercontinent was submerged for a while below the oceans, when it emerged as dry land this was mainly low lying flat land, and for this reason much of the land in the world today is indeed low lying and flat and why the Great Flood was able to

'...*cover the mountains to a depth of more than twenty feet*'
(Gen:7.20)

The Mid Atlantic Oceanic Ridge

When North and South America moved westwards and Africa and Europe moved eastward the basaltic shell formerly below these great land masses suddenly found itself relieved of a tremendous weight. As a consequence this part of the Earth's

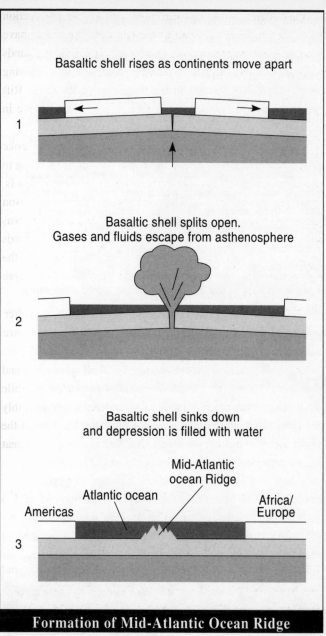

Formation of Mid-Atlantic Ocean Ridge

Fig. 9.3

basaltic shell was able to rise up even more and eventually ruptured, releasing an immense amount of material again in a flash of lightening and tremendous earthquakes. This event also caused a great loss of life.

After this release of pressure and material the shell sank down again forming another huge depression which was promptly filled in by the waters from the global ocean. In this way the Atlantic Ocean was formed. The rupture line has now been carefully mapped and is a well known feature called the Mid Atlantic Ocean Ridge which runs almost from the North Pole to the South Pole. The ridge is exactly half way between the separated land masses of the eastern (North & South America) and western parts (Africa & Europe) of the supercontinent. Fig 9.3. illustrates this.

Other ridges in the ocean beds of the world were formed in the same way but not all involved land movements.

The Mid Atlantic Ridge is incorrectly used by some Earth scientists as an illustration of how new material is formed at the ridge which somehow pushes the basaltic shell sideways and in doing so causes the shell to bend downwards into the Asthenosphere some thousands of kilometres away. This they say results in moving of the continents with the basaltic shell or plates acting as a conveyor belt. Using measurements of the rate of movement of the plates made only in the last few decades, they say that it must have taken millions of years for the continents to be where they are today. But common sense tells us that new material formed at a ridge does not have the pressure required to move the whole shell and if it did the new material would simply spew up upwards rather than spread out sideways. Currents in the Asthenosphere are also said to play a part in moving the shell, but it is hard to see why these currents should act in one direction only, when it seems more probable that if there are such currents they are more likely to be in random ever changing directions during the supposed hundreds of millions of years.

Associated with a ridge is what is called a trench, where one part of the basaltic shell has started to move under an adjacent part.

This mode of formation is consistent with the theory for the formation of the basaltic shell and the Asthenosphere that we have proposed. In fairness it must be said that it is not in accordance with the usual plate tectonics theory which postulates that plate movements are the results of current in the Asthenosphere and 'new' ocean floor is created at the ridge as the plates are subducted at the trenches.

Not surprisingly today the Earth's basaltic shell is no longer a complete intact shell, but has been broken up into plates. Ridges and trenches mark the boundaries of some of these plates. Movement between the plates still occur causing adjacent plates to rub against each other causing earthquakes and volcanic eruptions. This fact was realised a very long time ago.

'all the foundations of the earth are shaken' (Ps.82:5)

The movement of the plates today is quite small but does allow pent up energy to dissipate, and for this reason the Earth has remained in a relatively stable condition for the past three or four thousand years. Also the Moon is that much further away now so its effect has somewhat diminished a little.

Thus with all the continents in place and with all the oceans formed as described, the Earth became the planet as we find it today.

Once the stages of its construction are properly understood all the many physical features of the Earth like soil and rock formations can be can be adequately explained according to the theory we have advanced, but it would take another book to list and interpret all these features.

As a final note to this chapter we need to keep reminding ourselves that the land we live on was once part of a baby planet which crashed on to the Earth. Our land masses have still not fully settled down, and are still constantly being heated from below and have been immersed under the oceans at least twice.

There is some legendary evidence to suggest that the magnetic iron core of the crashed baby planet is where we would expect to find it- in the centre of the original supercontinent. If we take all the present continents of the world today and join them up like a jigsaw along the edges of their continental shelves we would get a near circular land mass. The centre of this land mass is close to the district of Magnesia in Greece. There are mythical stories from this area which tell of soldiers feet becoming stuck to the ground because of the iron studs and iron nails being pulled out of ships as a result of the strong magnetism of a mountain. Could there be some truth in these myths after all?

Further Reading
Whitcomb J C & Morris H M *The Genesis Flood* Baker Book House
Grand Rapids 1961
'Wilson J T *Continents Adrift and Continents Aground:Readings from Scientific American*
W H Freeman & Co. San Francisco 1976

CHAPTER TEN

THE END OF THE WORLD

'For a fire has been kindled by my wrath, one that burns to the realm of death below. It will devour the earth and its harvests and set on fire the foundations of the mountains.' (Deut. 32:22)

A planet under threat

Many people believe that the Earth is 4.5 billion years old and that if we look after it should last at least for a few hundred million years more. This being the widely accepted opinion, few people are inclined to take seriously the possibility that this planet could be utterly destroyed in much less time than this, as the Bible tells us plainly. In this chapter we look at the Biblical predictions about the future of the planet and this chapter is really intended only for those readers who can believe that every word in the Bible is true.

According to the theory that we have proposed in this book the Earth became inhabited by people only some 6000 years ago and bearing in mind the manner in which the Earth was formed, its behaviour in the recent past and the precarious balance of the Solar System in general, it would be optimistic to believe that the Earth will survive as a planet fit for human habitation for much longer.

We know of one catastrophe which killed the entire population of the Earth (except eight people) only about 4400 years ago and but for the foreknowledge of one man who survived with his family none of us would have been on this planet today. Further global catastrophes of terrifying proportions are predicted and, knowing how our planet is made these predictions seem quite logical.

There are three reasons for us to take the predictions made in

Firstly the formation and subsequent collapse of the Binary Sun has left a great deal of loose debris within the Solar System and there are still billions of asteroids of all sizes in orbit round the Sun which are still spiralling slowly inwards. Disaster can strike at almost anytime as a result of a collision between the Earth and a single or swarm of asteroids.

We know of at least two such swarms of asteroids with which the Earth ploughs through every year.

The first of these is the Leonid swarm which the Earth encounters in mid November each year. In 1833 the state of Alabama USA received a particularly violent shower of meteors from this swarm and the event gave rise to the song 'Stars fell on Alabama'. The swarm is really the remnants of a ring of asteroids orbiting the Sun at an angle to the Planetary Disc so that the Earth has to pass through this ring. In space the Leonid swarm has already begun to contract and this is bad news because it means that small asteroids are aggregating into large asteroids which one day could be in collision with the Earth. Every 33 years the Earth hits this particular swarm near its rather denser nucleus so that meteor bombardment from this swarm every 33 years is particularly intense. It was intense in 1966 and is expected to be intense again in 1999.

Another swarm of asteroids is the Perseids which the Earth encounters in mid August each year.

We often see very large asteroids better known as comets moving slowly across the night sky partially evaporating as they do.

Comets are a single or family of very large asteroids of ice with gas and dust. Throughout history man has treated comets with great fear and as a warning of some great disaster to come. We have already seen how massive comets can upset the delicate balance of the Earth's basaltic shell with catastrophic results, so the fear that man has for comets is not without foundation.

hundred years to several thousand years, and being dark objects until they get close enough to the Sun, they are difficult to detect and we have no means of having much by way of advance warning of their size and possible close encounter with the Earth.

Two major sources of comets have so far been identified. The first of these is called the Oort Cloud named after Jan Hendrik Oort, a Dutch Astronomer who postulated its existence in 1950. The Oort Cloud is thought to be some 15 billion kilometres from the Sun and is thought to consist of billions of giant ice/dust asteroids.

The second source of comets is The Kuiper Belt named after Gerard Kuiper who suggested its existence in 1951. This sphere of giant asteroids is thought to be 6 billion kilometres from the Sun.

The existence of these large asteroids is consistent with the manner of the formation of the Solar System as already described and they can also be regarded as remnants of the Binary Sun. It is possible that these asteroids will in time collapse to another ring and finally into two more planets like Jupiter or Saturn.

Both the Oort and Kuiper asteroids form a sort of a thick spherical zone that envelopes the entire Solar System. It is a zone which is getting heavier and closer because the whole of the Solar System is moving like a gigantic sphere of asteroids and planets around the galaxy collecting up huge quantities of interstellar gas and dust, and we must therefore expect swarms of asteroids to be dislodged from stable orbits and head towards the Sun or other planets including our own. This means that we could be engulfed by a swarm of asteroids at any time.

If such a giant mixture of gas, ices, dust, small, large and very large asteroids collides with the Earth the damage to the Earth would be very severe, although there would probably be enough survivors to carry on the human race. The Bible predicts such an event and we will examine this prediction later.

We need to be grateful to Planet Jupiter because its great mass example of this diversion in 1994 when the Comet Shoemaker-Levy family of asteroids was captured by the gravitational attraction of Jupiter and eventually hit this planet in a spectacular manner over a period of a few weeks.

The second reason for being pessimistic about the future of our planet is the close presence of our Moon. Our binary companion remains a threat by its ability to heat up the material under the basaltic shell which powers earthquakes and far worse catastrophes. The frequent earthquakes that the Earth experiences now is a testimony that all is not well in the hot molten material immediately below the solid basaltic shell of the Earth.

Furthermore the material immediately below the land masses on which we live is also in a fluid molten state and continents and islands are still capable of sliding about on top of the basaltic plates they are founded on, as well as move with the plates. Both mechanisms would lead to minor and major earthquakes.

Some scientists believe that the source of heat in the rocks below the basaltic shell is decay of radioactive material. Others believe that the heat arises because the Earth is still contracting under its own weight. But to these we must also add the heat generated by the Earth/Moon binary system and the heat generated by asteroid impact which is localised. Which of these sources of heat will be the dominant one does not really matter.

As long as the material below the basaltic shell remains in a hot fluid state, earthquakes of global proportions remain a serious possibility. The vertical movements involved could be severe enough to submerge some continents below the sea, as happened only about 4400 years ago.

The third reason for concern about the Earth's future is our Sun.

Although the Sun is the nearest star to us it is surprising how little we know about it. The problem of its source of heat has not been resolved to everyone's satisfaction. The belief that a thermonuclear reaction involving the conversion of hydrogen into helium is the source of heat is widely accepted but is probably not the full story. We have suggested that some of the heat from the Sun that we get at present is the result of continued contraction of gas, as well as an electrical process whereby electrons and protons are driven away at high speed from the three neutron cores in the sun and these fast moving particles make their way into space as the Solar Wind through a relatively thin layer of the photosphere, thus heating up this layer in much the same way as an electrical current heats up the element in an electrical light bulb or kettle. (See Appendix 5.)

We see evidence for the intensity of the Solar Wind when approaching asteroids made up of highly volatile material are heated and the resulting gases become hot enough to be lit up by this wind, and this gives the asteroid its characteristic visible tail pointing away from the Sun which we call a comet. Thus comets support the theory that it is the Solar Wind that provides some heat from the Sun at the present time. The Bible suggests that the world will be treated to a spectacular demonstration of the Solar wind in one of the events of the last years of this planet, and more about this later.

The danger to the Earth from the skies above is very great but we must also remember that less than 50km below our feet under the Earth's solid basaltic shell is an extremely hot ocean of molten rock and gases which also remains a serious threat to the continued safety of the world.

A close encounter with a gigantic asteroid swarm will not only cause havoc from above but could also trigger off eruptions from below and the final destruction of the Earth will, as suggested in the Bible, start by an asteroid invasion into our space but be completed by the extremely hot material that lies below the Earth's basaltic shell.

Predictions of an impending global catastrophe is not something that scientists would make without very careful study and they would therefore disassociate themselves from some of the seemingly wild predictions made in the Bible, but the message is quite clear that

> *'The earth will be completely laid waste and totally plundered.'* (Isa. 24:3)

Many people take this warning very seriously for themselves (because dead or alive at the time they believe that all be affected) and for their children, and also believe that there is something that can be done to save themselves from the series of global catastrophes that have been predicted for this planet.

The Great Tribulation

> *'For then there will be great distress, unequalled from the beginning of the world until now - and never to be equalled again.'* (Mat.24:21)

Destruction of a magnificent planet like ours seems hard to imagine and most people do not think it will happen in their lifetime and are not in the least bit worried about it.

According to the Bible the world will not end suddenly but there will be a period called the Great Tribulation which will last for seven years during which the population of the Earth will be almost completely wiped out by a series of catastrophes.

The Earth itself will not be destroyed by these catastrophes and will survive for a period of about a thousand years afterwards which will be a wonderful golden era called the Millennium, during which conditions for life will return once again to a near ideal state as they were right at the beginning when life started on this planet some six thousand years ago.

After the Millennium there will be no further use for the Earth. Our planet will have served its purpose and be set on fire and there will be no survivors. The completely devastated and dried up Earth will then become desolate and cratered like the Moon or the planet Mercury and the Sun will eventually claim it.

The events predicted in the Bible for the Great Tribulation and for the Millennium are consistent with the manner in which the Earth was formed as described in the preceding chapters.

The disasters to hit the Earth will include famines, earthquakes, asteroid bombardment and a Sun that will overheat. Each of these are catastrophes are discussed below in the order suggested by the Bible.

Famines and Earthquakes War and Plagues

'... there will be famines and earthquakes in various
places' (Mat. 24:7)

The first catastrophe of the Great Tribulation will happen quite gradually.

The population of the Earth is now over 6000 million and there is already great difficulty in ensuring that food supplies are produced and distributed as needed. Millions of people are on a starvation diet and the level of starvation is already much too high and will get worse.

As the Asthenosphere gets hotter earthquakes and volcanic eruptions will become more frequent. This will affect climatic conditions and food production and distribution even more in an overpopulated world and in the scramble for land and dwindling resources, wars will break out. Many people will die either from starvation or from epidemics or from the resulting wars in which nuclear and biological weapons are likely to be used.

This first catastrophe will claim the lives of one quarter of the Earths population - something in excess of 1500 million people.

'... they were given power over a fourth of the earth to kill by
sword, famine and plague.' (Rev. 6:8)

137

Asteroid bombardment

The second catastrophe will be extremely terrifying and will cause human suffering on an unprecedented scale.

'At that time the sign of the Son of Man will appear in the sky,and all the nations of the earth will mourn.' (Mat. 24:30)

The survivors of the famine and wars will remember the appearance of a comet or two earlier on and will probably blame these comets for the calamities that has fallen the world.

But as they gaze at the night sky even more comets and meteorites will be seen. Using space telescopes and spy satellites Astronomers will by this time confirm the worst fears that the earlier comets were mere forerunners of an extremely massive swarm of asteroids heading our way. Hasty calculations would reveal that the swarm is on its way to the Sun but would pass dangerously close to the Earth.

The whole swarm will become visible in the night sky and appear larger each night. At first it will appear as a mere speck of light but after a few weeks it would be much brighter and later on it would look like a distant galaxy. Finally it would occupy about a quarter of the night sky and there would then be no doubt then as to what it is.

The first effect of having a huge mass so close to the Earth will be an upset in the precarious balance of the Earth's basaltic shell. One large asteroid will impact the Earth and this will trigger off a massive earthquake

'There was a great earthquake' (Rev. 6:12)

Shortly after this the gigantic asteroid swarm will move past the Earth and partially block out the light from the sun,

'The sun turned black like sackcloth made of goat hair'
(Rev. 6:16)

and the dust within the swarm will give the Moon a crimson colour. Only in early 1997 a meteor shower in China caused the skies to go crimson for several days and something like this on a more massive scale is predicted for the time of the Great Tribulation.

> '... the whole moon turned blood red' (Rev. 6:12)

The Earth's gravitational pull will attract asteroids of all sizes from the swarm and these will impact several parts of the Earth

> '... and the stars in the sky fell to earth, as late figs drop from a fig tree when shaken by a strong wind' (Rev. 6:14)

The first encounter will also cause some loss of the Earth's atmosphere which will be pulled away by the combined gravity of the swarm

> 'The sky receded like a scroll, rolling up..'(Rev. 6:12)

and the Earth's basaltic shell will also respond to the gravitational pull of the swarm by widespread movements of the continents

> '... and every mountain and island was removed from its place'
> (Rev. 6:14)

Survivors will panic and attempt to take cover from the seemingly relentless meteor bombardment. Some will find breathing easier on higher ground. The bombardment will be so severe that the only protection from this will be in tunnels on higher ground that have not been blocked by the earthquakes or flooded by tidal waves. The scramble for suitable places of refuge will be great and the rich and powerful would seek to buy protection

> '.. the kings of the Earth, the princes, the generals, the rich, the mighty....hid in caves and among the rocks of the mountains.'
> (Rev. 6:15)

The first close encounter would cause severe damage to the Earth but the people who survive the first attack will have to brace themselves for another one as the swarm rounds the Sun and heads back towards the Earth.

The second encounter will result again in a tug of the Earth's basaltic shell causing more earthquakes as well as intensive meteor bombardment.

> '... there came peals of thunder, rumblings, flashes of lightening and an earthquake' (Rev. 8:5)

A particularly intensive meteor bombardment will affect a region of some 4500km in diameter. Everything in this region will be burnt by the resulting heat.

> '.. and it was hurled down upon the earth. A third of the earth was burned up, a third of the trees were burned up, and all the green grass was burned up.' (Rev. 8:7)

One particularly massive asteroid containing dust particles of red oxide of iron will enter the Earth's atmosphere and heat up tremendously before falling into the sea causing a huge tidal wave which will destroy all ships within thousands of kilometres of the impact.

> '... and something like a huge mountain all ablaze, was thrown into the sea. A third of the sea turned into blood, a third of the living creatures in the sea died, and a third of the ships were destroyed.' (Rev. 8:8)

Another very massive asteroid of similar composition, but containing radioactive material, will fall and pollute many rivers causing death to people which by now will have little by way of clean piped water.

'.. .and a great star blazing like a torch, fell from the sky on a third of the rivers ... and many people died from the waters that had become bitter.' (Rev. 8:10)

The giant asteroid swarm will spiral closer to the Sun and will now begin to orbit the Sun in an orbit somewhere between the orbits of Venus and Mercury. It is probable that both these planets will be absorbed by the swarm. By this stage the swarm will be very close to the sun and the solar wind will now be intense enough to attack individual asteroids within the swarm and cause them to partially vaporise. From a distance the asteroid swarm would look like a huge very dense cloud of gas in orbit close to the Sun. The cloud will partially shield the Earth from the full light of the Sun at least once each day and some of the planets will also be cut off from the Sun's light.

The Moon will also not receive the normal amount of light from the sun and some nights on Earth will be particularly dark, even on cloudless nights when the Moon would normally be a full one.

'... and a third of the sun was struck, a third of the moon, and a third of the stars, so that a third of them turned dark. A third of the day was without light...' (Rev. 8:12)

As expected not all of the giant swarm will be captured by the Sun. Stray asteroids will still find their way on to other planets and in particular the Earth.

The pull of the Earth will attract one large asteroid and this one will hit the Earth particularly violently and make a shaft like hole right through the already weakened basaltic shell.

'.. I saw a star that had fallen from the sky to the earth. The star was given the key to the shaft of the Abyss .. smoke rose from it ... The sun and sky were darkened by the smoke...' (Rev. 9:2)

The resulting pollution of the Earth's atmosphere will be so severe that a third of the survivors of past catastrophes will die from this one Earth shattering impact.

'A third of mankind was killed by the three plagues of fire, smoke and sulphur ...' (Rev. 9:18)

By this stage almost two thirds of the inhabitants will have died either by hunger, disease, poisoning or injuries sustained in the earthquakes, floods or bombardment by meteorites, but this will not be the end of the ordeal for the survivors.

Those who survive may have a spectacular glimpse of the attacking asteroid swarm in the night sky.

The swarm will split into two - a central portion made up of seven huge asteroids composed of mainly red dust with frozen gases, and an outer group consisting of twelve giant asteroids made from mainly frozen gases, but with a good quantity of dust as well.

The outer group will approach the Sun first and at one stage the solar wind from the Sun will give the combined asteroid group two tails, one made from gas and the other from dust, and as these tails reflect the light of the Sun they will look like the legs of a woman whose main body will be composed of a combination of the tails so as to look like a circular belly. The twelve asteroids will also reflect the Sun's light and the whole appearance will be that of a pregnant woman jewelled with twelve stones on her head. This shape of the asteroid swarm will coincide with the position of the moon at one stage so that the description of this image given in the book of Revelation will come true.

'A great and wondrous sign appeared in heaven: a woman clothed with the sun, with the moon under her feet and a crown of twelve stars on her head' (Rev: 12.1)

The second group of asteroids will soon after make itself visible in the sky. In this case there will be shorter tails like horns as well as a very long tail to the combined group. This group will be able to mop up some stray asteroids and some of these will now come under the Earth's gravitational pull, and once again the Earth will be bombarded by asteroids.

'An enormous red dragon with seven heads and ten horns and seven crown on his head. His tail swept up a third of the stars out of the sky and flung them to earth' (Rev. 12.3)

The Earth will next have to pass through part of the huge cloud of gas and red dust created when the inner swarm of asteroids was attacked by the solar wind.

This dust will fall as a thick layer over the entire surface of the Earth, causing death to marine and fresh water life

' ... the sea ... turned into blood ... and every living thing in the sea died ..... the rivers and springs of water ... became blood.'
(Rev. 16:3-4)

After several orbits in rapidly decreasing circles the giant swarm of asteroids and its gas and dust will finally crash into the Sun. The heat generated by this impact will be so great that thermonuclear reactions in the Sun will become uncontrolled, making the Sun very much hotter than it is at present.

'... and the sunlight will be seven times brighter...'
(Isa. 30:26)

The extremely hot sun will be too much for most people to bear.

'.. the sun was given power to scorch people ... They were seared by the intense heat' (Rev. 16:8-9)

143

The heat will be so great that no rain would fall anywhere on Earth and rivers will run dry after only a few weeks. The polar ice caps and mountain snow and ice will melt. Once again the entire Earth will be covered over with a thick canopy of water vapour and this will give some protection from the harmful rays of the now very turbulent and erratic sun.

As a result of countless asteroid impacts the heat generated in the material below the Earth's basaltic shell will again be very high and another pressure rise in the Asthenosphere will result, causing an upset of the precarious balance of one or more of the plates of the shell. These plates will rise quite suddenly and an extremely violent eruption will follow, with the ejection into the stratosphere of billions of tonnes of gas, vaporised rock and superheated steam. (The reader is reminded that not all the water from below the basaltic shell was released when the oceans were formed).

This explosion will be the cause of a very severe global earthquake in which tidal waves would flood over islands and continents. No city will escape damage. The basaltic shell would no longer be able to support high mountains and these would sink down within a day or two.

'Then there came flashes of lightning, rumblings, peals of thunder, and a severe earthquake. No earthquake like it has ever occurred since man has been on earth, so tremendous was the quake ... and the cities of the nations collapsed. Every island fled away and the mountains could not be found.' (Rev. 16:19-20)

Much of the water ejected will cool down in the high atmosphere and freeze and fall back all over the Earth in the form of giant hailstones of ice.

'From the sky huge hailstones of about a hundred pounds each fell upon men.' (Rev. 16:21)

144

The tremendous world wide ice fall will be the last event of the Great Tribulation but this will not be the end of the world as yet.

The Millennium

'They came to life and reigned with Christ for a thousand years'
(Rev. 20:4)

By this time there will be very few survivors left on the Earth, but the Earth itself will recover and become populated again very rapidly, mainly by a supernatural race of people.

The climate will be pleasantly warm throughout the Earth thanks to a vapour canopy and a still very hot sun.

The remaining land masses will once again become densely covered with vegetation and the oceans will teem with fish and animals will roam the Earth as they did at the beginning of creation. Human population will also increase once more, although all the vast technology and knowledge built up before the catastrophes will have been lost and people will once again lead simple mainly agricultural lives with plenty of land for everyone.

This golden era will last for a thousand years. After this time the material below the Earth's basaltic shell will again increase in temperature and the sun will again become unbearably hot. Human population will diminish rapidly.

Under this combined heat the oceans will gradually evaporate and the now very fierce solar wind will ensure that water is continuously driven off from the planet until all the oceans are dried up

'... and there was no longer any sea' (Rev. 21:1)

Conditions on Earth will become quite unsuited for human inhabitation and the entire population will either be wiped out or

145

else escape to another planet in a miraculous way that Nature will allow.

Deprived of the weight of the oceans the Earth's basaltic shell will once again rise up in several places and volcanic eruptions will take place throughout the Earth.

The Earth will be engulfed in smoke and flames and absolutely everything will be burnt up

> *'the elements will be destroyed by fire and the earth and everything in it will be laid bare'* (2 Peter 3:10)

And this will be end of Planet Earth.

Further Reading
Velikovsky I *Worlds in Collision* Gollancz, London 1950'
Sargeant D *Comets: Vagabonds of Space* Doubleday 1982

EPILOGUE

We have considered in the preceding chapters how Nature may have gone about the task of creating the Earth and allowed life in great abundance to flourish upon it. We cannot deny that Nature acted in a highly intelligent manner to have accomplished all this but we can still find it difficult to acknowledge this Nature as God.

Those who believe that it is blind Nature and not God that made the Earth and all life upon it have to admit that blind Nature does not appear to have sufficient intelligence or power to design and construct a planet or a life form in a predetermined manner and in a relatively short period of time. For these believers blind Nature has worked relentlessly by trial and error and accident over hundreds of millions of years. The purpose and final objective of blind nature cannot be fathomed out. Blind Nature cannot protect the Earth from destruction. We have seen how the Earth can easily be destroyed in a few days or weeks by a natural cataclysm. If this happens then all the hundreds of millions of years of evolution will have been a huge waste of time and to totally in vain. Blind Nature has no long term intentions for this planet and its life and will readily assist mankind to return to dust and ashes and oblivion. For people who believe in blind nature the past is meaningless and the future is frightening and bleak.

But true Nature, far from being blind, is an all seeing power and intelligence that can record the past and predict far into the future. Moreover the motivation of true Nature is love. For those who can believe this, the past becomes purposeful and meaningful and the future is exciting and something to look forward to. True Nature is none other than the Spirit of God.

The writer of the Bible seems to have struggled to find a suitable name for true Nature and simply calls it 'Word'. It seems fitting therefore to end the chapters of this book by quoting the Apostle John *(John 1-3)* who sums it all beautifully.

The Word in the beginning

In the beginning was the Word, and the Word was with God, and the
Word was God. He was with God in the beginning.

The Word as the Creator

Through him all things were made: without him nothing was made
that has been made

The Creator as the man Jesus

He was in the world and though the world was made through him,
the world did not recognise him.
The Word became flesh and made his dwelling among us

Jesus as man's only hope for continued life

For God so loved the world that he gave his one and only
begotten Son that whosoever believes in him
shall not perish but have eternal life.

And this brings us to the end of the story of the Earth's creation. The
rest of this book is devoted to Appendices which deal with more
technical and perhaps more speculative matters and is intended for
readers who may wish to explore the ideas expressed in the preceding
chapters in greater detail.

APPENDIX ONE

COSMOLOGY
- THE BIG BANG THEORY

Energy into matter

'In the beginning God ....'
(Gen. 1:1)

We live in a universe of galaxies. There are millions of galaxies, each containing billions of stars and separated from each other by thousands of light year, and still moving apart from each other at phenomenal velocities.

It is now generally accepted that the millions of galaxies in the Universe could have not always existed but must have come into being somehow at some period of time in the distant past.

Astronomers have long pondered over the question of how the galaxies came into existence and the problem is far from being solved. Did all the galaxies come into being suddenly a mere six thousand years ago as some Creationists believe? Or did the galaxies somehow condense out of the radiation and gas produced in a sudden explosion of energy called the Big Bang as some scientists believe? Or could they have simply grown into what they are today by accumulation of just one star at a time over a vast, almost eternal, period of time? These are questions that need to be addressed and answered in order to establish a firm foundation upon which to build our story of the Earth's creation.

But first a more fundamental question has to be asked and this is - did anything at all exist before any of the stars in the galaxies came into existence? If we say nothing existed we have a problem, because we would have to say that the galaxies formed from nothing, and many creationists would say that this is precisely the case, but not all scientists would be very happy about that. On the other hand if we say something existed the problem does not go away because we would have to define this something and make it amenable to scientific investigation.

As our starting point we can say that a good candidate for this something is a form of energy. But then we still have to explain the origin of this energy and we would have to admit that energy came from nothing.

Energy is the only starting point we can use, and if we can accept this, then all we have to do is to trace the transmutation of energy into matter.

Now matter has many forms - some very simple, others extremely complicated - but we can assume that if energy is transformed into matter this would have to be matter in its simplest form. Having the simplest form of matter as a starting point, it then becomes relatively easy to explain how this matter formed into the simplest gas and how this gas then went on to form galaxies of stars and how some stars gave birth to planets made up from exceedingly complex forms of matter.

Energy is something we know quite a lot about. It can exist in many forms, some of which we understand very well and use it in our everyday life. Other forms we know exist but do not understand. We certainly do not know very much about the first form of pure energy that existed in the very beginning. We can at least call it Primordial Energy.

We know that energy can be transformed from one form to another but cannot be created or destroyed. This is the well established law of the conservation of energy. It was only during the early part of this century that it was discovered that matter can be transformed into energy.

As matter can be transformed into known forms of energy then the law of energy conservation implies that energy can be transformed back into matter. But so far man has not been able to take known forms of energy and convert this into matter but perhaps one day he may learn how to do so.

Matter is energy. This very relevant and important statement is easily understood by considering something quite simple, for example an ice cube. On close examination of the cube we would find that it was made up of tiny particles called molecules with a measurable mass. If we were able to split one of these molecules we would find that it contained two atoms of hydrogen and one of oxygen both of which still have mass. Atoms are formed from even tinier particles called neutrons, protons and electrons and all these subatomic particles still have mass. This means that our ice cube is made up only of neutrons, protons and electrons. The mass of an electron is much smaller than the mass of a proton, and in many respects an electron behaves like a wave rather than a particle, but its energy can nevertheless be calculated. The proton and neutron can be split up again into even tinier particles, but these are found to have transient highly energetic wave like existences. Hence our ice cube is a complex tangle of highly energetic waves and is really a very complicated expression of energy.

Indeed all the matter we see around on the Earth today and throughout the Universe is composed of neutrons protons and electrons, and hence all forms of matter may be regarded as expressions of energy. A galaxy containing billions of stars is in the final analysis merely an expression of energy, so we may say that the entire Universe is an expression of its own primordial energy.

Hence it may be said that the physical Universe began at a certain point in time when there was a transformation and reorganisation of the eternal primordial energy into the energy we can touch and feel - the energy known as matter. Hence to understand the origin of the galaxies we need to understand exactly how, when, and why this energy transformation took place.

Two fairly well known theories have been proposed to suggest how this may have happened. Firstly we have the widely accepted but much criticised Big Bang Theory which has good supporting evidence in its favour but nevertheless does not explain nearly so much as some people think. Secondly we have the almost abandoned Steady State Theory which has virtually no supporting evidence, yet intuitively seems to make sense, and once had greater appeal than the Big Bang theory.

In this Appendix a brief outline of the main features of each of these theories is given, although neither of them are acceptable for our purposes, as they do not give satisfactory explanations for important observed features of the galaxies. However both theories have parts which seem reasonable and acceptable and we can use these parts as a basis for a third theory, which is proposed in Appendix 2.

The Big Bang that never was

'For the wisdom of this world is foolishness in God's sight'
(1. Cor. 3:19)

At the present time the most favoured theory on how the Universe began is what has come to be popularly known as the Big Bang Theory. It is a theory which has received much mathematical and physical examination and is undoubtedly the theory most widely accepted by Astrophysicists. But it has its critics and is not expected to survive much longer.

This theory took some sixty years or more to develop into what it is today. The first version of it was proposed not by a scientist but by a cleric - a Belgian priest Georges-Henri Lemaitre in 1927. That a cleric should have felt the need to propose a theory for the beginning of the Universe is worth a comment.

Lemaitre put forward the hypothesis of a primordial quantum of energy contained within a sphere some thousand million kilometres in diameter. Note he too felt the need to start with a form of energy. He used the term primordial atom to describe this enormous sphere of energy. This sphere, he suggested, expanded rapidly, creating space and matter as it did so. Most people would find this statement difficult to understand.

Lemaitre's theory was the only serious theory during the next two decades, which included the years of World War II when scientists had more pressing problems to consider.
But coming from a cleric and involving instantaneous creation, this first version of the Big bang theory seemed to support the idea of Divine Creation, which some atheistic scientists found difficult to accept.

It is thought that it was for this reason that Professor Hoyle and others proposed the Steady State Theory in 1948, which diverted attention away from the Big Bang for a while. The Steady State Theory advocated a slow, natural and continuous conversion of energy into matter and intuitively seemed more reasonable. The early sixties was a time when there was a quite a debate about the merits and shortcomings of both these theories. A blow was struck against the Steady State Theory in 1964 when two engineers working for a telephone company found that they were picking up an inexplicable heat radiation coming from all directions in space. The existence of such a radiation was one of the predictions of the Big Bang Theory and when it was discovered it gave this theory a boost it badly needed.

At about the same time confirmation that the galaxies were moving away from each other was made by several astronomers. This too suggested that as the galaxies appeared to be moving away from each other there must have been a time when they were much closer to each other. Astrophysicists began to toy with the idea that the galaxies were once all packed together in a small volume of infinite density. This idea needed a thorough understanding of the structure of matter and the physics of extremely small particles.

Quite independently in laboratories in Europe and America great advances were indeed made in the understanding of the structure of subatomic particles which are much smaller than the familiar electrons, protons and neutrons. The existence of particles of matter that had virtually no mass or volume made it theoretically possible to reduce the size of Lemaitre's huge primordial atom of energy to a sphere of negligible size.

Thus the existence of a background radiation, the evidence of galaxies moving apart from each other, and the evidence that matter in the form of pure energy could indeed be concentrated within a very small volume led to the modern version of the Big Bang Theory about thirty years ago. Since then there have been attempts to refine the theory.

The modern version of the Big Bang theory now reads something like this.

Some 10 to 20 billion years or so ago all the material required for the construction of the Universe emerged suddenly from a point of infinite density in an extremely hot, very dense exploding fireball of matter and radiation. The sequence of events is thought to be as follows.

In the first instant of time, matter in the form of elementary particles necessary to form the entire Universe, emerged from a tiny ball the size of a marble or smaller called a singularity. After a tiny fraction of a second the 'ball' expanded into millions of times its original size and at this stage the contained material consisted only of an incredibly dense mixture of elementary particles of radiation and matter.

After three minutes the ball of material expanded to about 50 million kilometres (Lemaitre's primordial atom) and this expansion caused the temperature to drop to about a billion degrees K. At this stage the elementary particles of matter were said to have become converted to about 70% hydrogen and 30% helium nuclei.

Some 700,000 years later the ball is said to have expanded to several thousand billion kilometres and the temperature within it is said to have dropped to 4000K.

At this stage the Universe consisted of a single but still rapidly expanding cloud of hydrogen and helium gas. Note how Lemaitre's sphere of energy now becomes an expanding sphere of extremely hot hydrogen and helium. Over the next few billion years this cloud of gas and radiation is said to have somehow fragmented and cooled almost completely and from this huge cloud somehow the galaxies of stars were formed.

The scenario described above stretches the imagination a little, but apart from the singularity it seems plausible and the enthusiasm for the Big Bang theory from many scientists is undoubtedly high. But there are serious difficulties which we can now mention.

Firstly the theory does not tell us what happened before the instant of the Big Bang. Defenders of the theory respond by stating that the known laws of physics do not apply before the Big Bang because space and time only began after it. Hence we are not allowed to ask about this because no answer can be given in terms that we can understand.

Secondly the theory does not explain why matter came to be concentrated at infinite density and what caused this matter to suddenly increase in temperature by billions of degrees.

Thirdly the theory does not explain why matter is not evenly distributed throughout the Universe. If the theory is correct we should now have a uniform distribution of matter throughout the Universe. But observations indicate that this is not so and the Universe is found to be not smooth with respect to density but very lumpy. Matter is not uniformly distributed but concentrated into galaxies formed on the surface of huge spherical voids, so that the overall structure of the Universe is 'sudsy' like a bowl of soapy water full of bubbles of all sizes.

The galaxies themselves are not uniformly distributed in space, as some regions of space have a greater intensity of galaxies than others.

Fourthly the theory does not readily explain how a uniformly expanding cloud of gas would result in the formation of galaxies of stars. To overcome this problem an addition to the theory had to be made. This proposes that somehow a disturbance was caused in the uniform cloud which sent shock waves throughout the cloud, causing local densification and hence galaxy formation. But this solution to the problem requires another event of some sort and we need an explanation for this event.

As these are all very basic unresolved problems we regard the Big Bang theory as an interesting speculation but, despite much evidence seemingly in its support, we must dismiss it as an unacceptable explanation for the beginning of the Universe.

Nature is highly intelligent and to create something as beautiful as our planet Earth by setting off an uncontrollable explosion does not somehow seem right.

The theory we propose in the next Appendix is that Nature created the Universe not all at once, but one star at a time, in an orchestrated highly organised manner over an unknown period of time. But before we do this we need to look at some of the facts that have been used in support for the Big Bang Theory, as the same facts can also be used to support the new theory outlined in the next Appendix.

Evidence claimed to be in favour of the Big Bang Theory

Despite its obvious shortcomings the Big Bang Theory has gained favour for two reasons. The first of these is that there is no other real contender, apart that is from the theory proposed in the next Appendix. The second reason is that there appears to be a considerable volume of observational data which fits the theory. In science there is a human tendency to interpret observed data in a way that lends support to a preconceived theory and this author suspects that this may be the case with the Big Bang theory.

This observational evidence is discussed below.

Galaxies appear to be receding from one another

Most of the galaxies we can observe appear to be moving away from our own, but some galaxies have been found to be moving towards us. We observe the velocities of other galaxies from our own so what we measure is the difference in velocity between the observed galaxy and our own. It is hardly surprising that galaxies have been found to moving away as well as towards us, and the reason for this is given in the next chapter.

The further away a galaxy is the faster is its Recession velocity

The inference from this observation is that the galaxies must have accelerated away from each other and must therefore have been closer to each other in the past. Hence the idea that all galaxies were once concentrated in a small volume of space and the idea of a singularity of infinite density. According to the Big Bang Theory, if we could reverse time we would see the galaxies coming together and the Universe becoming smaller and smaller and increasing in density until the density became infinite and the galaxies all became packed into a tiny volume. This only becomes credible if we make the assumption that as the galaxies came closer to each other, matter would progressively be converted back into energy and energy can be confined into a tiny sphere or singularity. According to the theory that we describe in Appendix 2, if time was reversed we would indeed see the galaxies coming closer together but each galaxy would also contain fewer and fewer stars, so that at the starting point there would be no singularity of infinite density

There is an abundance of helium gas in the Universe

This is, as the theory predicts due to the temperatures involved in the very early period after the Big Bang. Hydrogen is the simplest element in existence and consists of just one proton with an electron in orbit around it. If two hydrogen atoms can be made to impact each other with sufficient velocity it is thought that a fusion of the atoms takes place, resulting in the formation of an atom of helium. For this to happen temperatures in millions of degrees are required and because so much helium is detectable in the Universe, it is thought that such huge temperatures must have once existed. But there is another way for helium to form without the need for such high temperatures and this is explained in Appendix 2.

Deuterium (heavy hydrogen) is found in the gas between stars

Deuterium is like a hydrogen atom but it has in addition one neutron as well as a proton in its nucleus.

According to the Big Bang theory heavy hydrogen could only have formed at the very high initial temperatures (which means very high particle velocities), thought to have existed at the instant of creation. Because Deuterium can be detected in space the inference is that temperatures must have once been universally exceedingly high, but such high temperatures are also possible in localised regions for reasons that are explained in Appendix 2.

A background radiation of 3K can be measured

All bodies radiate heat in the form of tiny packets of energy waves called photons. The higher the temperature the more energetic are these photons and hence by measuring the wave length we can tell what the temperature of the radiating body is. Outer space may be regarded as a body radiating heat in this way and measurements of the wave length of the photons arriving on the Earth today suggest that the temperature of outer space is only about three degrees above absolute zero. This is thought to be the case, because Big Bang supporters say that the Universe has now cooled down to this temperature from its initial temperature of billions of degrees at the start. But another way of interpreting this background radiation is by assuming that the Universe has warmed up to 3K from near absolute zero. We would also get the same low energy photons arriving on the Earth today and hence the background radiation can be interpreted in two ways which suggests quite different ways in which our Universe started.

The above is a fairly formidable list of facts that have been interpreted to support the Big Bang Theory. But as with all theories in science facts alone are not enough to say that a particular theory is correct beyond any shadow of doubt. In Appendix 2 we propose an entirely different theory, which is in complete agreement with the above facts but is in the author's opinion a simpler theory for how intelligent Nature probably went about the task of creating a Universe of galaxies.

The Steady State Theory

This theory is also called the Theory of Continuous Creation and was proposed by Gold, Bondi and Hoyle in 1948, some twenty years after Lamaitre's version of the Primordial Atom Theory. It was Hoyle who gave the Cosmic Singularity theory the popular if not accurate and perhaps derisory Big Bang name which has stuck.

The steady state theory postulates that the average density of the Universe has always remained the same, whereas the Big Bang theory postulates that the average density of the Universe is steadily decreasing because the Universe is getting bigger all the time as the galaxies fly away from each other,

Hoyle proposed that space does indeed expand and because of this expansion more matter had to be created to keep the density constant. He proposed that matter in the form of a hydrogen atom (one proton with one electron) was created in each cubic metre of space every 10 billion years! This would make the Universe infinitely old.

The theory goes on to suggest that these atoms of hydrogen would then clump together by gravity and thus form clouds of hydrogen gas.

From these clouds it was postulated that stars and galaxies of stars would eventually form in some undefined manner.

When it was first proposed the Steady State theory was mildly welcomed, but it eventually ran out of favour when it was felt that although it was intuitively quite appealing there was no evidence in its support.

Both the Big Bang and Steady State theories require some sort of unknown process for the appearance of matter from nothing. In this respect it is not surprising that some scientists find the theory of continuous creation more appealing because it is easier to accept that all the matter present in the Universe today is the result of a process going on throughout the vastness of space over an immense period of time rather than the sudden seemingly miraculous creation of the Universe's entire stock of it in an instant of time, from nothing, and at one point in concentrated space.

Despite their inadequacies both the Big Bang and Steady State theories have served their purpose in making us think about the start of the Universe. But the fact remains that neither of these theories are entirely satisfactory on their own for explaining the beginning of the Universe and the subsequent formation of our planet to our satisfaction.

It is however possible to take the best of both existing theories and formulate a new one. This new theory is proposed in the Appendix that follows.

Further Reading
Silk J *The Big Bang* W H Freeman & Co. New York 1989
Weinberg S *The First Three Minutes: A modern View of the Origin of the Universe*
Basic Books New York 1977
Learner E *The Big Bang Never Happened* New York 1991

APPENDIX TWO

COSMOLOGY
- THE BINARY PARTICLE THEORY

'He.. stretched out the heavens by his understanding'
(Jer. 51:15)

The Dynamic Universe

Almost every object that we can observe in the skies above is not static but rotates and moves through space at great speed.

Our own planet rotates round its axis once every twenty four hours and rotates round the Sun once every year, and the whole of the Solar system rotates round the Milky Way Galaxy, which itself is hurtling through space away from other galaxies.

If we consider the rotation of the Earth alone this means that each person near the equator is moving at a velocity of over 1600km per hour, but if we include all the other velocities then we are all moving through space at several thousands of kilometres every hour.

The Sun itself rotates round its axis once about every 28 days and distant stars rotate about their binary companions. Some very small but very heavy objects believed to be spheres of densely compacted neutrons, also called neutron stars or pulsars, rotate extremely rapidly- for example the pulsar in the centre of the Crab Nebula rotates about 30 times every second! This rotation of pulsars is of great importance when we come to explain later why our Sun shines and the origin of the Solar wind.

All these rotations and movements have to be accounted for.

If we assume that the all stars and planets were originally very large rotating clouds of gas and dust then their rotation can easily be explained. But we need to know what caused the rotation of the clouds of gas and dust in the first place.

Our Sun began with the formation of an extremely large slowly rotating cloud of mainly hydrogen gas measuring many billions of kilometres from end to end. We explained in chapter three how from this rotating cloud a rotating double star was formed, and how from this double star our Sun and all the planets, and in particular the Earth, was formed.

To explain the formation and features of this double star (called the Binary Sun) we need to begin with a cloud of hydrogen gas that is vast, has a slow but sure rotation, is steadily contracting under its own gravity, and is moving away from its point of origin.

Neither the Big Bang nor the Steady State Theories gives a satisfactory explanation for a cloud with all these features, so we need another theory for it and any explanation that we can offer for the origin of such a cloud must also explain all the main features of the Universe.

The Binary Particle Theory

'He determines the number of the stars and calls them each by name' (Ps.147:4)

This Appendix proposes a new theory for the formation of vast, moving and rotating clouds of hydrogen gas, and the name Binary Particle Theory has been given to this theory. The theory is new and may seem rather speculative, but the evidence for it is very good and this is discussed later.

The word binary means involving two parts and binary systems feature largely in the Universe at all scales, from the tiniest atom of hydrogen where we have a little electron in orbit round a proton to binary stars where two stars orbit each other, and binary galaxies and even binary clusters of galaxies.

Nature seems to like the idea of pairs that make a whole. Male and female, positive and negative charges in electricity, north and south poles in magnetism and so on are some

162

examples. It seems logical therefore to look for a binary system that led to the formation of the Universe's first ever rotating moving cloud of hydrogen gas and billions of other similar clouds after this one.

Very briefly this new theory postulates that Nature created the Universe in an intelligent orderly yet quite natural way by using its own primordial energy in a controlled calculated manner.

This idea is explained below.

The Laws of Nature

The Universe is governed by precise and reliable laws which scientists have strived for centuries to discover and understand. These laws exist because they have been carefully thought out and ordered to come into operation by a highly intelligent mind that has complete power and control of the entire stock of energy in the Universe. While some scientists would call this mind 'Nature' other scientists know it to be none other than the Mind of God. Nature is a manifestation of the spirit of God. Thus anyone who wants to know God can begin by looking at all that nature has accomplished and this includes both the physical creation and the laws of nature that allowed it to come into being and sustains the creation today. If we can accept that there is an intelligent mind that makes the rules and can also control energy by thought alone then the problem of the start of the material Universe becomes much easier to solve.

Primordial Energy

Before the material Universe began the only thing that existed was the Mind of God and primordial energy. We know that matter and energy are interchangeable. On Earth there is now no primordial energy so we can only change existing matter into energy but we cannot as yet do the reverse.

Astrophysicists agree that the material universe started by a transformation of primordial energy into matter. Big Bang theorists say that this conversion was an instantaneous uncontrolled and unavoidable event. However in this Appendix we suggest that the conversion was a premeditated gradual and highly controlled operation. Knowing the Mind that brought the laws of nature into being it is more logical to assume that the conversion of energy into matter was not an accidental event but a deliberate act of design and creation.

The first atom of hydrogen

Hydrogen is the simplest of all the elements and if there was a transformation of primordial energy into stable matter it is logical to assume that one of the first forms of matter would be hydrogen. An atom of hydrogen is a binary system and consists of one negatively charged electron in orbit round a positively charged proton. Hence we need an explanation for how the electron and proton came into existence.

Electrons and protons can be broken down into even tinier particles but if this is done these particles have very transient wave like existences which we can regard as expressions of energy rather than matter.

Energy can be converted from one form to another but never destroyed. In the beginning the entire Universe contained nothing but primordial energy ready to be converted into other forms of energy.

Nature began the process of construction of the material Universe quite simply by allowing a tiny bit of primordial energy to be converted into a proton. The power of thought over energy would be able to do this. In the same way and some distance away Nature allowed another tiny bit of primordial energy to become an electron. Another way of looking at this is to assume that primordial energy is electrically neutral but can be split into a positive part and a negative part which can be transformed into the proton and electron respectively. The separation involves the creation of space.

Once the first proton and electron were formed, each of these particles became subject to the laws of nature and this being the case they were obliged to act accordingly.

They responded as expected to the laws of gravity and electromagnetism and were instantly attracted to each other. The attraction allowed each tiny particle to acquire a high velocity so that the two particles approached each other across the created space and collided but they did not stick to each other but rebounded. After several collisions stability was attained with the two particles rotating about each other in a tiny binary system. Thus the first atom of hydrogen came into existence.

Electrons and proton replication and multiplication

The first atom of hydrogen was as expected completely surrounded by primordial energy and thus had to obey another law of nature which was to feed off the surrounding primordial energy and to replicate itself. The power of replication in living organisms is readily observable if the correct nutrients are readily available and the same instructions and power exists in non living atoms if surrounded with the right nutrient-in this case primordial energy.

Each of the constituents of the first hydrogen atom (the electron and proton) had built in instructions to make a perfect copy of itself and the copies themselves contained the same instructions and were thus able to continue the process of replication.

Thus each proton absorbed primordial energy and created more protons and each electron created more electrons. As in each replication primordial energy was used up, space was simultaneously created which meant that the distance between the original electron and proton increased. Space was thus inflated as suggested by both the Big Bang and Steady State theories.

The original single proton thus developed into a dense rapidly expanding spherical cloud of protons and, now at a great distance apart, the original electron developed into a dense rapidly expanding spherical cloud of electrons. The replication was true in every detail so that each newly formed electron and proton also inherited the movement of its parent particle.

The net result of all this conversion of primordial energy was a dense but expanding cloud of electrons rotating around a dense but expanding cloud of protons. Hence one tiny binary system consisting of a single hydrogen atom grew into a gigantic binary system consisting of two immensely dense but expanding clouds of tiny particles each rotating round the other exactly like in the first original atom of hydrogen.

Expanding Spheres of Electrons and Protons

The Universe thus began not with one extremely hot singularity but with one extremely cold binary system of two expanding spheres of matter - a positively charged dense but expanding sphere of freshly reproduced protons and a negatively charged dense expanding sphere of electrons, with each sphere rotating around each other.

We need to consider each of these spheres in a little more detail.

In the positively charged sphere primordial energy was converted at first into a wide range of fundamental subatomic particles, most of which on their own had unstable transient existences only, but some of these then combined to form stable protons in vast quantities.

It is important to appreciate that before stable protons could emerge from the source a host of even smaller particles had to

166

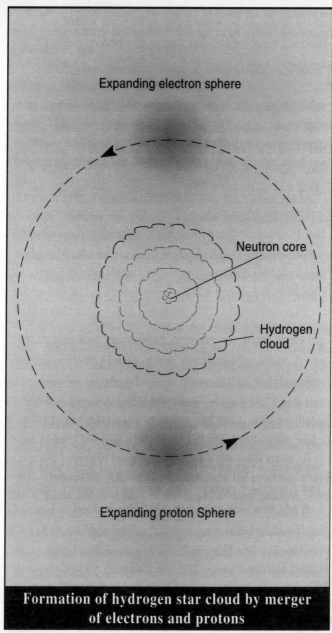

Formation of hydrogen star cloud by merger
of electrons and protons

Fig. A2.1

form first. These smaller particles of necessity had very transient existences and reverted back into the pool of primordial energy almost as soon as they emerged, and this was as Nature intended to deliberately control the rate of proton production.

The protons were produced at a controlled steady rate and emerged from the source at a high enough velocity to be able to be projected into empty space in all directions. In this way the protons (and other subatomic particles) formed a dense sphere which began to expand very rapidly not unlike the manner suggested by Lemaitre in his description of the Primeval Atom. The expansion was facilitated by the fact that particles with the same charge repel each other and that space had to expand to accommodate all the newly created matter. The conversion rate was slow, to minimise gravitational pull on the newly formed protons. A large gravitational pull would have prevented the protons from being scattered into the vacuum in the surrounding expanding space.

While proton production went on at one sphere of the first binary system, a similar process took place in the other sphere.

Here fundamental subatomic particles again emerged from the electron producing source, but these also had transient existences until they were able to combine to form stable electrons. Thus electrons in vast quantities were produced in a steady controlled manner. These electrons radiated into space in all directions, again forming a rapidly expanding Lemaitre type near spherical shaped cloud of fast moving electrons. The expansion was ensured by virtue of the natural repulsion between electrons and the fact that each electron had an initial velocity as soon as it was formed, and the controlled rate of electron production also kept gravitational forces down so as not to impede the expulsion of the newly formed electrons, and the expansion was again into a vacuum now devoid even of primordial energy.

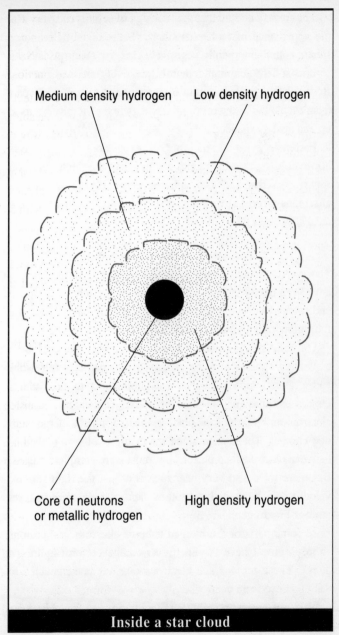

Inside a star cloud

Fig. A2.2

169

Thus it may be said that the first sign of activity in space was the appearance of two expanding spheres of particles - one sphere containing mainly negatively charged electrons and the second sphere containing mainly positively charged protons. Both spheres rotated around each other but also moved apart from each other as the primordial energy in the vicinity got used up and space expanded.

Fortunately for us the rate of expansion of space was however lower than the rate of expansion of the electron/proton spheres so that the two spheres eventually grew into an enormous size until they invaded each other's space. Figure A2.1 illustrates this.

Formation of the core of a star

The two expanding spheres of electrons and protons would have been barely visible but where the two spheres overlapped and merged into each other an observer may have detected a faint glow of activity.

Only in that region of space shared by parts of both expanding spheres was the density of the particles (electrons and protons) high enough for combinations to take place. Untold billions of billions of close encounters between electrons and protons took place as the two spheres merged into one another. There were some direct high velocity collisions between electrons and protons but most were complete misses. But there were also very near misses at just the right relative velocity which resulted in protons capturing electrons to form atoms of hydrogen.

In some parts of the merged spheres electrons and protons simply did not have the energy to escape or form hydrogen atoms. These protons and electrons thus became impacted to each other to form neutrons.

Vast quantities of neutrons were formed in this way. Neutrons may be regarded as tiny magnets, so once formed their own magnetism ensured that the neutrons would clump together quickly. In this way neutrons attracted neutrons and clumped together to form a huge core of tightly packed neutrons. The core as a whole retained all the angular momentum that the individual neutrons had before capture and as these neutrons were once widely scattered and now concentrated into a relatively small core, its final rotation rate was extremely high. There are hundreds of rapidly rotating extremely dense spheres of neutrons in our Milky Way galaxy and these have been found to have extremely powerful magnetic fields and to rotate several times a second. Astronomers know them today as pulsars or neutron stars but many Astronomers believe that these neutron stars are the remains of dead stars and not the beginnings of a star as is suggested here.

The main task of the core was to ensure that its own very considerable gravity would also attract most of the hydrogen that was also formed around it.

The magnetism of the neutron core and its extremely rapid rotation are features which are of crucial importance in understanding why our own star, the Sun, produces heat and behaves in the way it does.

Formation of a star cloud

Around the core vast quantities of hydrogen were formed by the coupling of electrons and protons, and the heavy neutron core was instrumental in allowing this to happen by slowing down and deflecting protons and electrons. The core was also able to prevent a good proportion of the newly formed hydrogen from being blown into oblivion.

In an ordinary hydrogen atom there is just one proton in the nucleus with one electron in orbit, but if a neutron becomes attached to a proton and has an electron in orbit around it, then what is called heavy hydrogen or Deuterium is formed. If aggregation is taken a stage further and two protons combine with two neutrons and attracts two electrons another gas called helium is formed.

Hence the cloud of matter resulting from the merger of the two expanding spheres of electrons and protons consisted of mainly hydrogen but also had significant proportions of deuterium and helium all gravitationally bound by the core of compacted neutrons.

The term star cloud may be used for this cloud because it is from a cloud such as this, consisting mainly of hydrogen and helium but with a heavy core of neutrons, that each star of the Universe including, our Sun was formed.

In regions where there was no overlap of the expanding electron and proton spheres there were either too many protons or too many electrons or the particle density was too low to enable sufficient encounters between the electrons and protons to take place, and for this reason only a little hydrogen and helium was formed in these regions.

We can gain some idea of the shape of the star cloud.

As the star cloud was formed only in the merged regions of two immensely large expanding electron/proton spheres the region of overlap was egg shaped. But as the electron/proton spheres rotated about each other, the star cloud also became more or less spherical.

The star cloud grew in mass very rapidly and gravitational forces became dominant and allowed it to contract.

This caused the density of the cloud to increase.

But at the same time the cloud was subject to continued bombardment by both electrons and by protons and this caused the cloud to experience a sort of 'wind' pressure. The wind pressure was greater on one side of the cloud than the other as

172

a result of the much greater mass of the particles of protons. Hence under this uneven pressure the cloud began to move away from its point of origin. As the direction of the proton 'wind' pressure also changed continually this had the effect of giving the cloud a slow but sure rotation. Thus the cloud began not only to rotate but also to drift away into truly empty space. And so moving, rotating and contracting clouds of hydrogen and helium came into existence and each of these clouds went on to become a single, binary or triple star as explained a little later on.

Formation of the galaxies

The whole process of the formation of star clouds described above was repeated untold billions of times and one by one star clouds appeared like puffs of smoke but held together by a hidden neutron core. Driven by the cosmic wind these enormous clouds drifted majestically into space in all directions.

Each star cloud so formed came under the influence of two dominant forces. The first of these was the continued pressure from the 'wind' of protons from the positive energy source and under this pressure alone the cloud began its long journey into empty space.

The second force was the gravitational attraction of all other clouds that were formed earlier on. Under the action of these two forces all star clouds found themselves blown towards and attracted towards other previously formed star clouds and in this way immense groups of star clouds were formed. Many of these star clouds eventually contracted into stars and thus the galaxies of stars began to form.

The proton 'wind' also affected star clouds, even once in the safe harbour within a galaxy. This meant that the whole galaxy suffered the same fate, and galaxies were also blown towards

The Sudsy Universe.
Each white speck is a galaxy. Note the
concentration of galaxies and large empty voids.

Fig. A2.3

174

and attracted by other galaxies, and in this way clusters of galaxies were formed. The process did not end there. Clusters of galaxies were blown and attracted to other clusters and thus superclusters of galaxies were formed.

And thus the Universe as we know it came into existence-one star cloud after another and one star after another, and galaxies increasing in size and mass and number all the time. This process began before the first day when time for mortals on Earth began. Like happenings in the night the galaxies were formed over an unknown period of eternal time.

In support of the Binary Particle Theory

To conclude this Appendix a listing some of the facts which tend to support Binary Particle Theory for the formation of the Universe is given.

Fact 1 Invisible dark matter.

Today we know by calculations and observations that the parts of the Universe that we can actually see constitute only a tiny fraction of what is actually present. Many Astronomers believe that we can only see about one per cent of the matter within range of our optical and radio telescopes, so that 99% of all the matter in the Universe remains hidden from view.

The seemingly lost material has come to be known as hidden dark matter, which is now a major problem and field of study in Astronomy. No one is absolutely sure what all this hidden dark matter really is, and there are several suggested possible candidates.

But according to the Binary Particle Theory that we have outlined in this appendix the quantity of hidden dark matter is not unexpected. The material Universe was formed one star at a time in conditions of extreme cold barely a few degrees above absolute zero. During formation of each star an immense amount

175

of matter in the form of protons and electrons was simply wasted (see Figure A2.1) and now lies somewhere as a halo at the outer boundaries of the galaxies.

Another form of dark matter is simply extremely large bodies of frozen and liquid hydrogen (like the planet Jupiter) which have not as yet been transformed to light and heat emitting stars. Billions of Jupiter like objects probably exist throughout our galaxy and in other galaxies, but being too far from a light emitting star such objects would be virtually undetectable.

Still more hidden dark matter is in the 'halos' that are believed to completely envelope all galaxies. The presence of this halo has puzzled some Astronomers, but according to the Binary Particle Theory this halo is entirely as expected because the halo is the result of free electrons, neutrons and protons whose velocity was not great enough for them to escape the gravitational pull of the Galaxy and were thus trapped where we find them today. The amount of material in the halo is thought to be very considerable as the motions of individual stars within the galaxy appear to be affected by it. Galaxy halos are actually a very important part of the galaxy. Without them many more galaxies would have collapsed prematurely into a single massive black hole and become invisible. Much has been written on the existence of black holes. According to the Binary Particle Theory black holes are again hardly surprising. They are not very old objects which were thought to be the remnants of dead stars but are simply very young collapsed stars and galaxies which did not have either the necessary rotation or the halo to counteract gravitational collapse. There should be quite a few of these objects within our own local group of galaxies and it is only a matter of time before the techniques for their detection will improve to enable us to locate them.

Fact 2 The sudsy Universe

Today many of the galaxies emit sufficient light to be photographed so we can now discern not only the shape of some of the galaxies but also obtain a map of the night sky showing how these galaxies are distributed in space.

Such a map very dramatically and clearly shows a sudsy universe with spherical voids of all sizes and galaxies arranged around the edges of the voids. The overall picture is not dissimilar to a bowl of aerated soapy water and for this reason the structure of our Universe is called sudsy as shown in Figure A2.3.

A sudsy Universe is what we would expect from the manner in which it was formed. The newly formed protostar clouds were blown into space to find a home within a galaxy of other stars as described earlier in this chapter and the sudsy overall structure of the Universe is exactly as expected and is an indication of the strength and ferocity of the cosmic wind.

Fact 3 The expanding Universe

Hundreds of observations during the last seventy years or so have confirmed beyond reasonable doubt that the galaxies are moving apart from each other. The actual rate at which this is happening is not certain as different astronomers arrive at somewhat different results. The main problem is the estimation of the distance of each galaxy from our own and other galaxies. A few observations suggest that in some cases galaxies are actually moving towards us rather than away from us but overall the Universe seems to be expanding. Some astronomers have interpreted this expansion as an expansion of space and this is a possibility. But according to the Binary Energy Theory the moving apart of the galaxies is as expected because each newly formed star cloud was blown into truly empty space and into galaxies and the resultant galaxies and cluster of galaxies are still continuing to move under the momentum they acquired from each member star cloud.

Another important fact about the rate at which the galaxies are moving apart has been discovered. This is that the rate is neither too fast nor too slow. If it was any slower the galaxies would come together again and that would be the end of the Universe. Such a system is called a closed Universe. If the rate was too high the expansion would go on and on forever and we would have what is called an open Universe.

But according to the Binary Particle Theory the movement of the galaxies was caused by 'wind' pressure from protons escaping from a reserve of energy at just the right velocity. Hence it is not surprising that the galaxies move at just the right velocity. For this reason there is now almost an exact state of balance and hence astronomers have not been able to decide whether we live in a closed Universe or in an open one.

Fact 4 Cosmic Wind

According to the Binary Particle Theory each star was formed from a stream of protons and electrons moving in opposite directions. This stream of protons and electrons continues to this day. We are now very far away from the source so the intensity is much reduced as may be expected. Nevertheless our galaxy and the Earth is still bombarded continuously by this stream of particles. These particles are quite lethal and capable of killing all forms of life within a short period of time. But fortunately for us the effect of this continual bombardment is minimised because of the protection that our atmosphere provides. We have learnt to use these Cosmic rays to determine the age of some objects on the Earth. This is possible because the upper layers of Carbon Dioxide in our atmosphere absorb some of the neutrons and changes the carbon in the gas into an unstable radioactive form. We make use of this fact in the carbon dating techniques.

Analysis of the particles that hit us continually show that they come from outside the Solar System and are made from pure protons, pure electrons and combined double proton/neutron pairs. The term Cosmic Rays is really a misnomer because it is not an electromagnetic ray like light or radio waves or X rays, but is a high velocity wind made up of streams of tiny primordial particles - the evidence which supports the existence of Binary Particle sources of electrons and protons and their later combinations.

The existence of Cosmic Wind is thus another indication that the Universe began in effect by intense Cosmic Wind activity as described. This intensity has decreased as expected quite drastically because we are that much further away from the source but still continues to this very day.

It is quite probable that the Cosmic Wind that reaches the earth today is of secondary origin and comes mainly from the millions of bright stars within our own galaxy.

Fact 5 The microwave background radiation

The average temperature of space can be measured by simply pointing a radio telescope in a particular direction and then recording the frequency and length of the waves it picks up. From this information it is possible to say what the average temperature of space is in that particular line of sight. Scientists who have done this found that the temperature recorded in all directions is about three degrees above absolute zero which is very cold indeed. This observation of temperature is in agreement with the Binary Particle Theory in which some heat was generated when electrons and protons were propelled into space. This very small temperature has been used by supporters of the Big Bang Theory as evidence of a remnant echo of the Bang itself. They say that the Universe began as an extremely hot fire ball which has since expanded and cooled so that we

179

can now measure the temperature of the ball some billions of years later.

But according to the Binary Particle Theory the Universe began in extremely low temperature conditions and has remained so since then so what we measure today is this very low temperature.

Fact 6 The great cosine in the sky

There is another aspect of the microwave radiation that has not been given the attention it deserves. This is the fact that the recorded temperature of space is not strictly constant but varies slightly (and with great precision) with the direction in which the temperature is made. The temperature reaches a maximum value in one direction and a minimum value in exactly the opposite direction. The temperature can be measured in any direction and if this done the results can be plotted on a graph of direction against temperature. The resultant plot is of the same shape as the plot of the cosine of an angle with the angle itself and for this reason the temperature/direction graph is called the great cosine in the sky. In space temperature is an indication of the number of particle to particle collisions. The more collisions the higher the temperature. Hence the very small temperature variation in space means that there is one direction in which more particle to particle collisions occur than in the opposite direction.

The existence of this temperature variation is as expected if the Universe originated according to the Binary Particle Theory because from Figure A2.1 it is clear that the intensity of particle collisions must vary from a maximum value near the particle sources to a minimum value further away. Since a probe on or near the Earth can only measure the intensity of the radiation over a very short distance it is not surprising that the variation is indeed very small but measurable. It is fair to add that some astronomers attribute this very slight temperature difference to the way it is measured taking into account the rotation of the Earth.

Fact 7 The velocity of the galaxies

Astronomers are now able to analyse the light received from distant galaxies and determine from this the relative velocity between that galaxy and the Earth. The velocity of many galaxies have been determined in this way and although there is some doubt about the accuracy of these measurements, the general conclusion from this work is that velocity of the galaxy depends directly on how far the galaxy is away. Galaxies close to us are moving slower than galaxies far from us. The ratio of the velocity to the distance is called Hubble's Constant after the person who first suggested this relationship. The Binary Particle Theory gives a good explanation why such a relationship exists and this is discussed briefly below.

During and immediately after formation each star was subject to a 'wind' pressure from the intense bombardment by cosmic rays. Tiny pressures acting over an exceedingly large area amount to a sizeable force and force acting on any body causes that body to accelerate. The acceleration depends on the mass of the body (in this case the star cloud) and we can be sure that the mass of the star cloud must have been many billions of tonnes. Consequently the acceleration should have been very low. Calculations based on observed galaxy velocities confirm that although the velocities are now very high the acceleration is indeed very low and unmeasurable over a period of an astronomer's lifetime.

Measurement of the distance and velocity of a galaxy is fraught with difficulties but there appears to be a linear relationship between the distance of a galaxy and its velocity. This is simply because galaxies most distant from us were formed early and hence have by now gained a higher relative velocity than galaxies closer to us which were formed later although it is likely that all galaxies had the same very low acceleration after they were formed.

Fact 8 Pulsars

Aggregations of clumped neutrons which have become small but very dense and rapidly rotating bodies have been discovered in several locations within our galaxy. These are rapidly rotating bodies which are highly magnetic and rotate very rapidly - some times several times a second. They are also called pulsars.

Current theory is that pulsars are Neutron stars which were once very large clouds of hydrogen which contracted to such an extent that the electrons of the hydrogen atom became impacted into the protons to form neutrons.

According to the Binary Particle Theory we should indeed be expected to find aggregations of rapidly rotating neutron cores, which by virtue of their rapid rotation, have not been able to hold any appreciable amounts of non magnetic material by gravity alone because such material would have simply spun off.

Fact 9 The rotation of the galaxies

All galaxies rotate. If they did not the member stars would quickly attract one another and the whole galaxy would become an enormous black hole.

According to the Binary Particle Theory this rotation is entirely as expected because galaxies were formed from moving rotating star clouds and the momentum of these clouds is now reflected in the momentum of the galaxy itself. The rotation of the Earth can be traced right back to the rotation of the star cloud that eventually became the star called the Binary Sun.

Binary Particle or Big Bang Theory?

We have discussed the Big Bang Theory and the Binary Particle Theory rather briefly. The Big Bang Theory is well documented and several books on the subject are available. The weakness of the Binary Particle Theory is that it is based on pure intuition and the unproven idea of Nature designing and willing into existence the first atom of hydrogen and allowing this atom to stretch apart and reproduce itself by forming a positive proton producing part and a negative electron producing part as described. The circumstantial evidence for this theory is as good if not better than other theories but for some critics this may not be enough. The weakness of the Big Bang Theory is the idea that Nature acted in rather a chaotic manner and that out of the disorder of the Big Bang somehow order came into being.

When one considers that there are billions of galaxies each containing billions of stars it is difficult to see why all this vast amount of matter had to be created in a few seconds of unimaginable chaos with no provision for sorting out the mess. Nature knows better than this how to create a Universe!

The idea of galaxies moving apart from each other is not difficult to accept but the idea of expanding space carrying with it the galaxies is more difficult to understand. Hoyle's idea of space expanding to allow matter to form so that the density of the Universe remains constant would fit in with the Binary Particle theory except that it seems more logical to assume that if primordial energy is concentrated in a particle of matter then the space around the particle must be truly empty and space therefore has to expand.

The Binary Particle Theory explains why galaxies are moving apart but this would have happened even if empty space did not expand.

183

The Binary Particle Theory is too new to gain any serious recognition. But our consolation is that the observed data does seem to fit and it does enable us to understand how moving, rotating clouds of hydrogen with built in rapidly rotating very dense cores of neutrons were formed.

The core is of crucial importance and the Binary Particle Theory does explain why such clouds have a core of very dense neutrons and why this core is also very highly magnetic.

From one such cloud our Sun was formed and from this the Solar System was formed in a dramatic way that was described in the chapters of this book.

The idea that the Universe was formed not all at once but in puffs of gas, one cloud at a time in an orchestrated controlled manner over an almost eternal incalculable period of time from primordial energy, is perhaps more appealing than the idea of the entire Universe appearing in a fraction of a second from one point of infinite density.

In conclusion to this appendix we may stress once again that we set out to find an explanation for the origin of a vast, moving and rotating star cloud with a rapidly rotating core at its centre and if we can either simply accept that such a cloud came into existence in another way or by an unknown manner or accept the explanation for such a cloud given in this Appendix then our story of the Earth's creation can start where it did.

Further Reading
Lemaitre Georges *The Primeval Atom* Van Nostrand New York 1950
Roordan M & Schramm *The Shadows of Creation: Dark Matter and the Structure of the Universe* W H Freeman & Co New York 1991
Webster A *The Cosmic Background Radiation* Scientific American August 1974

APPENDIX THREE

THE UNIVERSE OF GALAXIES

'Look up at the heavens and count the stars - if indeed you can count them' (Gen. 15:4)

Features of galaxies.

In Appendix Two we saw how large rotating and moving clouds of mainly hydrogen were formed when an expanding sphere of electrons merged with an expanding sphere of protons and how the clouds contracted into stars either before or after they were blown towards a group of existing stars to become part of a galaxy.

In our own galaxy the Milky Way there are believed to be over 300,000,000 Sun-like stars. Our galaxy rotates and because of this our Sun takes about 200 million years to make a complete orbit round the centre of the galaxy. Moreover the whole of our galaxy rotates with other galaxies in our cluster around a common centre of gravity. All this rotation is merely a manifestation of the rotation of the electron/proton spheres which supplied the energy to form each star in the galaxy. Rotating, moving galaxies of immense size illustrate wonderfully the power and intelligence of Nature.

The Milky Way Galaxy is one of about thirty galaxies of our Local Group Cluster but the distribution of the galaxies in the cluster is such that the whole system can be regarded as a binary cluster because it really consists of two very large galaxies (The Milky Way Galaxy and The Andromeda Galaxy) which rotate about each other, and these two major galaxies each have satellite galaxies. The Andromeda Galaxy is now moving towards the Milky Way Galaxy and we are heading for a collision which would result in the collapse of this particular binary system.

The Milky Way Galaxy and its retinue of satellite galaxies has been gravitationally captured by The Andromeda Galaxy and its retinue of satellite galaxies and for this reason the two giant galaxies are hurtling towards each other.

On a much much smaller scale our Moon was formed separately from the Earth but was later captured by our planet.

We can look at our Milky Way Galaxy with the naked eye. We are positioned very near to one of its stars (the Sun) and can therefore look out at night at the other stars within our galaxy. Our galaxy is disc shaped with a bulge in the middle. If the disc was absolutely flat we would see it in the night sky as an arc like a rainbow of diffused light right across the sky from horizon to horizon. But because it is a thick disc we see our galaxy as a band of closely spaced stars - so seemingly close to each other that their light forms a belt of milky diffused light- hence the name of our galaxy.

The disc shape of our galaxy is of some relevance to the story of the Earth's creation. The reason for this is that the planets of the Solar System were formed from an immense cloud of gas and dust. This cloud also became disc shaped like the shape of our galaxy but only a few billion times smaller. The term Planetary Cloud was used for the cloud from which the planets were formed and we had much to say about this cloud. Each star of our Milky Way galaxy can be regarded in the same way as clump of dust in the Planetary Cloud but apart from a vast difference in scale there are similarities in behaviour.

There are millions of galaxies in the night sky for us to study. Many of these galaxies have been viewed with very powerful telescopes and excellent photographs of them taken.

All galaxies that we can study have light emitting stars and while we cannot see individual stars in these distant galaxies we can make out the overall shape of the galaxy.

story of the Earth's creation because these shapes may be regarded as the various stages in the contraction of an extremely large collection of stars. Each star in a galaxy moves in the same way as a small asteroid in a large swarm of asteroids in space and the overall shapes that apply to a large collection of stars in a galaxy as they come closer together by gravitational attraction apply equally well to a collection of asteroids in space. Thousands of photographs of galaxies have been taken and these reveal a number of features which are very relevant to the Earth's formation and some of the more relevant of these features are described below.

The first feature that strikes us about a galaxy is the obvious fact that it is composed of millions of stars, each of which was blown into the galaxy and became part of it over an eternal period of time. This fact illustrates firstly the power of gravity and secondly the power of the cosmic wind. Both these factors need to be considered when we come to describing how the Earth was formed. Each new star increases the attractive power of a galaxy by increasing its overall mass. This makes it more difficult for other wandering stars to escape the clutches of a galaxy and the galaxy is thus able to mop up wandering stars and like a snowball, grow quite quickly. Our Milky Way galaxy alone made over three hundred million captures of wandering stars, and possibly ten or twenty times more of star clouds which have not as yet become light emitting stars and remain as dark matter, which is thought to account for at least 90% of the total mass of the galaxy.

In the same way as we explained in detail earlier on, the formation of the Earth began with the clumping together of iron dust to form iron asteroids. These asteroids then formed a swarm which aggregated by gravity and magnetism to form a huge sphere of iron. This great ball of iron now forms the innermost core of our planet.

As this core grew in size it became progressively easier for it to attract other lighter material and in this way our planet was built up layer by layer by gravity alone as described in this book.

The second important feature of many galaxies is that near their centre or nucleus there is a concentration of stars and thick dust. This tells us that the galaxy is still contracting and that the central nucleus is winning its battle to grow in size by gradually pulling in stars.

The nucleus acts like a magnet and attracts individual stars to it and, like sediments in water going down a plughole, millions of stars become absorbed by the nucleus in this way.

Again on a much smaller scale this also illustrates how the core of our planet was built up. Whereas at the centre of a galaxy there is a 'core,' probably in the form of a black hole, at the centre of our planet we have a giant red ball in the form of a heavy core of magnetic iron oxide.

There can be little doubt that a galactic nucleus has suffered many collisions. It is in fact extremely difficult to see galactic centres as hundreds of collisions have resulted in the nucleus being shrouded with collision debris consisting of clouds of thick dust that cannot be penetrated by optical means. Our planet was also shrouded in dust at all stages of its formation as a result of continual asteroid bombardment and most of the thick deposits of clay, silt and sand that now cover the Earth's surface are as a result of countless billions of asteroid collisions with our growing planet.

A third important feature of galaxies is that they do not occur singly but as multiple systems all rotating around each other about a common centre of gravity. The planes of rotation and the orbital distances of each galaxy from the centre of rotation are such that collision between galaxies is a possibility and there is good evidence that even today some galaxies are actually colliding with each other.

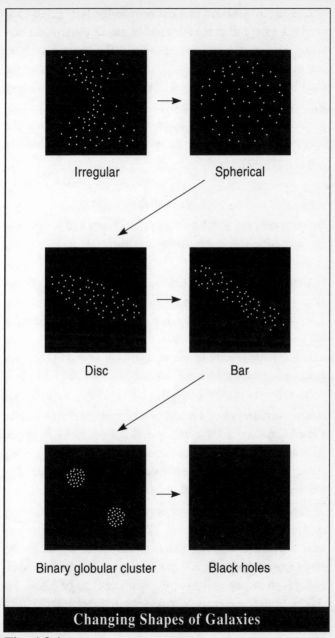

Changing Shapes of Galaxies

Fig. A3.1

It is highly probable that our own Milky Way galaxy was involved in a collision with another galaxy from our Local Group which it has since absorbed. This may also have contributed to the formation of our planet by disturbing the equilibrium of a binary star. The next collision of our Galaxy will be with The Andromeda Galaxy but thankfully this will not be during our lifetime, but when it comes a least a few of the binary stars in both galaxies will probably collapse and result in planet formation.

Galaxy shapes

Galaxies come in about a dozen or so shapes and we need to consider these shapes because this is also relevant to how our planet was formed.

Galaxies are not in the main an irregular collection of stars as one would expect, bearing in mind their mode of formation. The overall shape probably was highly irregular to begin with, but as a result of gravitational, centrifugal and cosmic wind forces any irregularity of shape is quickly ironed out and the galaxy settles down for a while - and only a while - into one of about a dozen different shapes.

The overall shape of a galaxy gives important clues about the age of a galaxy. So, for example, a highly irregular shaped galaxy would be regarded as having a large proportion of very young stars but a cigar shaped galaxy would be regarded as an old one and towards the end of its development.

The shape of a galaxy is not easy to ascertain because we are only able to view it from one side. Thus a spherical galaxy would appear to us as circular disc and a disc shaped galaxy could appear to us as cigar shaped if we viewed it from the sides rather from the top or bottom. But with millions of galaxies to choose from the chances of looking at different galaxies from different angles is good.

The first person to make a systematic study of galaxies and their shapes was Edwin Hubble, a young legal executive from Kentucky who in 1922 gave up his profession as a lawyer to study Astronomy. He became fascinated by the shapes of the galaxies that he could observe with fairly modest telescopes and catalogued and classified them. In doing so he made no attempt to suggest how the shape of a galaxy is related to its age and development. But now we can simulate galaxy behaviour on supercomputers and so we can study galaxy development and shapes on a screen in armchair comfort which is somewhat more convenient than waiting for a clear night to take photographs of different galaxies and then discern their shapes.

A big advantage with computers also is that we are in complete charge of the time factor so that movement over millions of years can be plotted in a matter of a few days or weeks.

Hence we can take Hubble's classification of galaxy shapes and rearrange them in order of their state of development.

Hubble classified galaxies into about seventeen types depending on shape and whether or not they had spirals. For our purposes we can reclassify them into just four types as follows

Type 1 ....Irregular

Type 2 ....Spherical

Type 3 ....Disc

Type 4 ....Bar

Now if any of the above types have been in a recent collision with another galaxy four new types of galaxy shapes form as follows

Type 1a ....Irregular with spirals

Type 2a ....Spherical with spirals

Type 3a ....Disc with spirals

Type 4a ....Bar with spirals

Computer modelling of galaxy collisions clearly show spirals developing after collision and this is also confirmed by observations of colliding galaxies.

The four types of galaxy shapes listed above are in the order of increasing age. All galaxies start as an irregular arrangement of stars. After some time gravitational forces build up a nucleus and this helps to smooth out the irregularities of the overall shape. The galaxy then becomes near spherical with a possible bulge around its 'equator' where centrifugal forces are the highest. Our planet also has a slight bulge round its equator for the same reason.

After a further period of time the spherical galaxy flattens in stages and becomes disc shaped.

By this time the now disc shaped galaxy may have suffered some loss of its overall angular momentum, so that within the disc the centrifugal forces are not as high as they used to be and this allows the disc to contract inwards to form a bar shaped galaxy. The bar then contracts to form two globular structures of stars and becomes a dumbbell shaped galaxy. Such shaped galaxies have been reported and globular structures are the most magnificent objects to be observed in the night sky, but they are not very common because by this time the concentration of stars in each end of the 'dumbbell' is so great that each 'dumbbell' collapses into binary blackholes and disappears from view altogether. Out in space there should be hundreds of binary blackholes but they are impossible to detect with the techniques we have developed so far.

All this tells us that any rotating galaxy could eventually end up as a binary galaxy before the binary collapses into a single galaxy and then finally into a very massive black hole.

What happens to stars in a galaxy also happens on a much smaller scale to a swarm of asteroids and it is asteroids that concerns us most when we come to understand the Earth's creation.

Binary galaxies tell us that we should expect to find in each galaxy plenty of binary stars. The behaviour of a gas cloud in space is not dependant on its size. We have binary galaxies and binary stars within a galaxy. And on an even much smaller scale we have binary planets and we have much to say about this later on.

Galaxy collisions

Collision between galaxies is not an uncommon occurrence and is entirely expected, bearing in mind that all galaxies are part of a cluster of galaxies which rotate about a common centre of gravity. This is a precariously balanced system that is easily upset. The orbits of any two galaxies within the same cluster may easily intersect.

Thus galaxies in the same cluster may be expected to eventually collide. It may be argued that clusters with a large number of member galaxies are comparatively young and those with a few members of galaxies are older as in these clusters absorption of one galaxy by another is quite likely to have taken place.

Collision between galaxies are not really very dramatic events. Because of the vast distances between stars within each of the colliding galaxies the collision takes place with only some star to star collisions.There is however an undoubted interaction of gravitational forces and for this reason galaxies emerge after collision essentially unaltered in shape except for the dislocation of some of the stars in the outer regions. These are thrown outwards by the collision and thus form long tails or curves of stars called spiral arms. Some Astronomers believe that these spiral arms are made up of stars freshly formed from the gas contained in both galaxies. This observation is in accordance with the Binary Particle theory for the formation of the Universe, because a galaxy is a region in which 'puffs' of hydrogen clouds from their point of origin would tend to collect, and collision between galaxy and galaxy would result in collisions between hydrogen clouds resulting in a massive output of light which we observe as stars.

Computer simulations of galaxy collisions show that existing stars also experience disturbance in the orbits that they had previously acquired within the galaxy.

Spherical or disc galaxies which have been in a recent collision display long open spirals. In time these spirals close up and become moderately wound. The closing up of the arms continues for some time and the galaxy is then said to have tightly wound spirals. Finally all traces of the spiral arms will have disappeared and the galaxy will have returned to its original shape smothered in fresh gas and dust from the numerous star and dark matter collisions, but otherwise it would be difficult to tell at this stage that the galaxy had been in collision with another.

The discovery that the spiral arms of a galaxy have concentrations of gas and dust is a very important one since our Sun is in a spiral arm of our galaxy. The presence of gas and dust concentrations in spirals is very relevant and important to the story of the Earths creation because without this additional gas and dust the spectacular event that triggered off the formation of the Solar System may never have happened. This stupendous event was described earlier on.

The Milky Way Galaxy to which we belong may be classified as a disc shaped galaxy with open spirals. Two of these spirals can be seen at different times of the year snaking across from horizon to horizon in the night sky.

The implication of the shape of our galaxy is that it has been in a recent collision and we should be thankful for this, as otherwise there might have been no planet Earth in this part of our galaxy.

In conclusion we can say that galaxies give us some important clues as to how our planet Earth was formed and these may be summarised as follows

1. Gravity is able to act over immense distances and although over these immense distances the attractive force is extremely small the cumulative effects are quite spectacular. With regard to the Earth's formation we had to consider the effects of the Sun's gravity and the Cosmic Wind on extremely tiny particles of dust and gas.

2. An irregular shaped rotating galaxy becomes a disc shaped one. This is of relevance because the cloud of gas and dust from which the Solar System was formed also had an irregular shape to begin with and this then contracted into a disc shape, and we had much to say about this disc earlier on in this book.

3. Rotating galaxies sometimes become binary galaxies and the formation of binary stars and binary planets is an important feature of this story of the Earth's creation.

4. Collisions between galaxies are not uncommon. Collisions between bodies of planet size are also not uncommon and as far as the Earth is concerned we had much to say about a very important collision which led to the formation of a supercontinent on this planet.

5. The Universe is made up of galaxies but as galaxies grew star by star and galaxies have collided with each other and exchanged or acquired new stars in the process, the age of the galaxy cannot be determined by the age of a particular star. All galaxies may be expected to contain stars of all ages and for this reason, although the Milky Way Galaxy may be very old, our Sun is very much younger and our planet is also very young.

6. Galaxies tells us how star size bodies eventually converge into the central nucleus. This gives us a picture of how asteroids also converge to form planets such as the Earth.

7. Finally all galaxies are in the process of contracting into a single very massive body or enormous black hole. There will be a time when each galaxy will be reduced to an unimaginably massive black hole. All these black holes can be expected to behave as one enormous universal galaxy of black holes. Galaxy behaviour will be repeated again and this enormous Universal galaxy of black holes will finally become a binary system with just two gigantic black holes each containing half the mass of the entire Universe and rotating about each other. Perhaps by then the black holes will be so massive that they would be something as close to pure energy that we could get to. The Universe will thus end as it began in a binary system of two energies.

And then perhaps the two energies will start materialising again into protons and electrons all over again and a new Universe will come into existence. Perhaps.

Further Reading
Hodge P *Galaxies* Havard University Press 1986

APPENDIX FOUR

FROM HYDROGEN TO EVERYTHING

...'the heavens existed and the earth was formed out of water and by water' (2 Pet. 3:5)

Formation of the elements

In the Chapter Four we described how the Binary Sun collapsed into a single body which became enveloped by an immensely large very hot cloud of collision debris consisting of gas and dust which we called the Planetary Cloud.

The Earth and all the other planets were formed from this Cloud in a manner that was described in Chapters 4 to 6.

In this Appendix we explain how this cloud, formed by the collision between two bodies made up of mainly hydrogen and helium came to contain all the necessary elements required to form materials like water, air, soil, rocks and metals of all kinds of which the planets are constructed.

Hydrogen and helium were the main elements in the original cloud from which the Binary Sun was formed. But our planet, in common with other planets, is made from thousands of different combinations of a little more than hundred different elements and any account of the Earth's creation must therefore include an explanation of not only how these elements came to be formed but also how they came to be present and sorted out into useful concentrations on each planet.

In this Appendix we describe how the hundred plus elements were formed and we explain also how these elements and their chemical combinations were able to become concentrated at various locations in the Planetary Cloud and how, while there, they were able to combine with others to form concentrations of all kinds of planet building materials, including precious metals like gold and silver.

197

Stars as element factories ?

There are a little over a hundred known different elements to be found on the Earth and we know a great deal about each of them in terms of their make up and how and why they can combine with other elements to form an almost limitless number of very stable materials. The science of Chemistry tells us how and why elements combine chemically with other elements, but the actual origin of these elements is still something of a mystery to most people.

It is only now that we understand the structure of the atom and the energies involved in its construction that we have come to realise that very few if any of the elements could have been made on the Earth and most of them, if not all, must therefore have come from elsewhere.

The simplest element is hydrogen. According to the Binary Particle Theory Appendix 2) for the origin of each star in the Universe, the formation of hydrogen atoms is easily explained as a binary electrical union of a positively charged proton in the nucleus with a negatively charged electron in orbit around it. Helium, which is the next simplest element, was also formed in less abundance at the same time for reasons we have already given.

But as for the origin of the other elements, scientists have had to think hard.

The currently favoured theory for the origin of the rest of the elements heavier than helium is that they were created deep inside massive stars. According to this theory a first generation star forms when a cloud of hydrogen contracts into a solid body using its own gravity. This contraction results in an increase in both pressures and temperature deep inside the interior of the star and these eventually become so great that hydrogen atoms are 'cooked' and become fused together to become Helium, Carbon, Oxygen, Silicon and Iron in the order given. So according to this theory stars of advanced age develop a core of iron surrounded in turn by thick shells of Silicon, Oxygen, Carbon, Helium and finally unaltered Hydrogen in its outermost layers. This part of the theory seems reasonable enough but it has not been proven by observation.

The theory then suggests that after a star develops an iron core and layers described above, it is eventually destroyed in a supernova explosion and the elements already formed are scattered into space. These elements are said to then become mopped up by passing hydrogen gas clouds which have not yet formed into stars and then this 'polluted' cloud containing supernova debris contracts to become a second or even third generation star. With a Universe believed to be anything up to 15 billion years old, advocates of this theory say this allows sufficient time for a first generation star to form, manufacture various elements and then explode and for the explosion debris to reform again into a second generation star and explode once more and so on until an explosion of a well developed third or fourth generation star produces all the necessary elements necessary to build a planet.

This latter part of the theory for element formation is less plausible and on closer scrutiny there are at least two problems with it.

Firstly there is no reason why the debris created in a supernova explosion should become part of a new star when simple calculations show that any such material is more likely to either contract back to the star of its origin or be dispersed and scattered into space, and once dispersed into space the amount of debris attracted by another hydrogen cloud would be negligibly small.

Secondly the idea of elements created inside stars and exported in a disordered supernova explosion does not explain how the scattered and randomly distributed elements manage to become separated out into useful concentrations for planet making. If there was no sorting out then our planet would not have been what it is and be similar to other planets and consist of a homogeneous mixture of everything. We would not have had the unique atmosphere we have or concentrates such as metallic ores and mines for gold and silver. Even concentrated deposits of sand and clay would be a rarity on our planet.

As these are not small problems we must reject parts of the theory of element formation inside stars and think afresh about this problem.

Element formation and the Binary Sun Collapse

The formation of all the elements from just hydrogen requires two conditions. Firstly we need exceedingly high temperatures and pressures of a magnitude almost impossible to attain here on Earth. Secondly we need (for the heavier elements) a fierce and continuous spray of fast moving free protons and electrons and neutrons.

The idea of collapsing binary stars and collision between star sized bodies in space has not as yet been fully accepted and for this reason it has not been appreciated that the tremendously high temperatures and pressures required for element formation is present not only deep inside massive stars but also on the collision contact surfaces of quite ordinary stars and even large asteroids when such bodies become involved in a high speed collision with each other or with another massive body.

As there was no supernova explosion involved in the creation of the cloud from which the Binary Sun was formed we can reasonably assume that the two components of the Binary Sun were composed of mainly original hydrogen and helium to start with, but it is quite feasible that because of the tremendous size and masses of both components of the Binary Sun the pressures deep inside these components was sufficient to cook and fuse some of the helium and hydrogen into other elements, and the current theory for element formation would support this view. This fusion process is described a little later

A very important consequence of the collapse of the Binary Sun was the sudden generation of stupendously high temperatures and pressures. These were high enough for the conversion of some of the hydrogen and helium into many (but not all) of the remaining elements so that some additional fusion elements were formed immediately after the collision.

When Solar A and Solar B came close together the mutual gravitational attraction was sufficient for parts of both the bodies to be loosened and torn apart, even before actual contact.

Hence some heavier elements which had been formed inside each component as current theory tells us were released from the depths of the smaller component (Solar B) even before the final stage of the collapse.

But when the Binary Sun finally collapsed there was a conversion of energies from kinetic to heat. The kinetic energy involved in the two very massive bodies rotating round each other and rotating round their own axis as well was enormous. On collision only part of this kinetic energy remained unchanged and the rest was converted to heat, light and radiation. Temperatures of hundreds of millions of degrees and pressures of millions of isobars were generated instantaneously by the collapse.

Pressures and temperatures equivalent to those that are thought to exist deep inside massive stars were thus created on impact. Under these conditions nuclei of preexisting hydrogen and helium were able to fuse together and entirely new elements were formed as explained further on in this Appendix

The collapse of the Binary Sun also happened at a time when the cosmic ray intensity was still very high. The collapse itself resulted in a radiation of free electrons and protons. Hence any elements that were not or could not be formed immediately by fusion during the impact were formed a little later in the resulting Planetary Cloud by another process called spallation, which is also explained as follows.

201

Fusion and spallation

The atoms of all elements consist of a nucleus containing protons and neutrons, with electrons in orbit around the nucleus. The total number of electrons in an atom of a stable element equals the number of protons in the nucleus and this number is called the Atomic number.

The electrons orbit the nucleus very rapidly in different planes and thus form a spherical barrier round the nucleus. This spherical barrier is generally known as a shell which protects the nucleus from intruders. To remove this protection very high temperatures are required and once the shell is removed the nucleus becomes vulnerable and can either lose or gain protons and neutrons.

Hence the simplest way of generating one element from another is to strip the element of its protective shell of electrons and then add or take away the requisite number of protons and neutrons in the nucleus. Having done this it would be necessary to reintroduce the required new number of electrons so as to form the protective shell once more.

This change of one element into another by electron removal, proton and neutron addition or subtraction and replacement of electrons is fairly simple to understand, but of course very difficult to accomplish in practice. If it were not so we would all be changing iron or copper into gold or some other precious metal!

Electron removal and proton/neutron addition requires conditions that cannot be easily attained here on Earth but takes place deep inside massive stars and after collision between massive bodies in space by one of two methods called fusion and spallation.

The conditions for fusion were fulfilled during the formation of the components of the Binary Sun and the conditions for both fusion and spallation were fulfilled when the Binary Sun collapsed.

Fusion

The fusion process is one in which a nucleus of an atom without its protective shell of electrons is brought into contact with the nucleus of another atom at such a high pressure that the two nuclei join or fuse together to become the bare nucleus of a totally different element. This is quite different from the usual way by which elements chemically combine where it is the electrons which facilitate the linkage by sharing the same shell of electrons but the individual nuclei remain unchanged and the final product is a molecule of some kind but not another element. Chemical combinations can take place at fairly low pressures and temperatures whereas fusion requires temperatures that must be high enough to strip off the shell of electrons and pressures that then allow one stripped off nucleus to impact into another. If the pressure is not high enough the two nuclei will simply repel each other and avoid a head on collision and no new element will form.

Fusion can create most of the elements in the Periodic table up to and including iron, but not elements heavier than iron. The reason for this is that once a nucleus reaches a certain size it becomes somewhat unwieldy and further attempts at fusion only succeed in a break up of the nucleus already formed.

During formation of the two components of the Binary Sun temperature and pressure conditions for the fusion of hydrogen and helium into heavier elements and for the fusion of these heavy elements into even heavier elements existed for short periods, because the formation of the two components involved not only the contraction of very large masses of freshly made hydrogen but also billions of collisions between large asteroids of frozen hydrogen and the conversion of kinetic energy into heat.

Further fusion of hydrogen and other newly formed elements took place when the Binary Sun collapsed, and by this time enough fusion elements to build a planetary system were created in prodigious amounts in a fairly random unsorted way.

Some of the more important and common elements formed in this way are described later on in this Appendix.

Element formation by spallation

For elements heavier than iron to form, the nuclei of elements already formed by fusion process can only get heavier if the nuclei remain stripped of its electrons and is then subjected to a rather gentle impact by individual neutrons and protons.

For this to happen the newly formed fusion elements must firstly be ionised, which means that the temperature must be high enough to drive away all the electrons. Secondly the bare nucleus must be allowed to grow rather quickly by the addition of individual neutrons and protons, and for this to happen there has to be a plentiful supply of these particles travelling slowly enough to be captured by the growing nucleus.

Such conditions prevailed within the Planetary Cloud which initially was at a very high temperature and therefore rich with the nuclei of fusion elements. Immediately after formation the nuclei of these elements became exposed and thus vulnerable to the attentions of individual protons and neutrons.

There were two sources of these neutrons and protons. The first of these was the cosmic wind, which at the time of the Binary Sun collapse was still very fierce because it was still quite close to the source of the radiation that created it in the first place. The second source was the cores of the collapsed binary which had a plentiful supply of these particles and still do today, which we call the Solar Wind.

Thus the Planetary Cloud already containing dust size particles of fusion elements now became irradiated with protons, neutrons and electrons and under these conditions the process of forming nuclei and atoms of the heavier elements from the lighter fusion elements was able to continue.

This process of addition of protons and neutrons to a nucleus is called the spallation process for element formation and a few examples of elements formed in this way are given later on in this Appendix.

It must be stressed that both methods of element formation (fusion and spallation) also took place to a certain extent even before the collapse of the Binary Sun. Both Solar A and Solar B probably had quantities of fusion elements according to the theory for element formation deep inside the stars.

But the second time for elements to form was towards the latter stages of formation of Solar A and Solar B, when there were millions of high speed impacts between large asteroids of frozen hydrogen and the asteroids that had already aggregated into a growing central body. At this stage of the accretion process these impacts would have been violent enough to fuse some of the hydrogen and helium into heavier elements. Each collision was accompanied by clouds of high temperature dust and each cloud of dust was relentlessly bombarded by cosmic rays. Hence during the formation of the Binary Sun the formation of some of all of the elements also took place.

But most of the elements were formed when the Binary Sun collapsed, and the magnitude of this collision was such that it is thought that a good proportion of the elements now present in the Earth and other planets were created by this cataclysmic event.

With these ideas in mind we can now consider the formation of some of the more important elements relevant to the Earth's creation.

Hydrogen and Helium

According to the Binary Particle Theory star formation began as a result of the coming together of protons and electrons to form hydrogen. But in certain locations within a star cloud electrons were also able to impact protons to form neutrons.

In an atom of ordinary hydrogen there is just one proton in the nucleus with one electron in orbit round the nucleus. But Hydrogen also has an isotope called Deuterium which has a neutron in the nucleus. For this isotope to form a hydrogen atom must acquire a neutron, and in a neutron rich environment about one in 30,000 hydrogen atoms became affected in this way. The existence of Deuterium in interstellar gases would tend to support the Binary Particle Theory.

Another isotope of hydrogen is Tritium. This is hydrogen with two neutrons in the nucleus. This isotope is as expected rarer than Deuterium and is not difficult to see how a Deuterium atom could have acquired another neutron in a high temperature hydrogen rich atmosphere irradiated with high velocity neutrons.

As Hydrogen was so easily formed it is not surprising that it is also the most abundant element in the Universe and there are still vast clouds of it in the Universe today.

The Helium atom has two neutrons and two protons in its nucleus and two electrons in orbit. It is the second most common element after hydrogen and was most formed quite simply as a result of a high speed collision between two Deuterium atoms when the star cloud was first formed. Helium can also be formed by fusing together of two hydrogen atoms. In this process a very tiny amount of mass is destroyed which is converted to heat energy which makes it possible for further elements to form.

Helium production by this process in a star like our Sun does not normally begin immediately after the star is formed, as it takes a while for the temperature deep inside the star to rise high enough.

It has been calculated that for every one Helium atom in the Universe there are about thirteen Hydrogen atoms. Bearing in mind its ease of formation in a concentration of fast moving electrons, protons and neutrons it is only to be expected that Helium is the second most common element in the Universe.

Oxygen
Oxygen is the third most common element in the Universe and

nucleus, with eight electrons in orbit. Oxygen is made by fusing together four helium atoms. This requires the helium atoms to be stripped of their electrons and to collide with each other with a velocity that would be attained by these nuclei if heated to a temperature approaching ten million degrees. It is unlikely that such a velocity existed in the cloud from which the Binary Sun was formed. But when the cloud began to form into two bodies as described, a tremendous amount of heat and pressure was generated and temperatures approaching ten million degrees could have been attained locally on both bodies during formation.

At the contact surfaces pressures in excess of the pressure at the centre of a typical star would be created as a result of the force of the impact, and even if the collision was a 'soft' landing the static pressure at the contact surface would still be very high as a result of the masses of the two components.

At the contact surfaces new helium atoms as well as previously present helium atoms were able to fuse with each other thus forming atoms of oxygen.

There is one oxygen atom for every about one hundred and fifty atoms of helium in the Universe.

Water, water everywhere

As hydrogen and oxygen easily combine to form water this was one of the main constituents of both Solar A and Solar B. Thus when the Binary Sun was formed there was already sufficient water formed by fusion as a result of the numerous collisions that occurred in the formation of the components. Both parts of the Binary Sun thus had vast quantities of water and on collapse of the Binary Sun some of this water was also partly converted into the other elements by the processes of fusion and spallation. The Bible verse at the top of this Appendix implies that all the elements were made from water and this is not inconsistent with what we know about element formation.

Carbon and silicon

Carbon is the fourth most abundant element in the Universe. This element has six neutrons and six to eight protons in its nucleus with six electrons in orbit. Its nucleus may be regarded as a fusion between three helium nuclei.

Carbon and oxygen react chemically together to form carbon dioxide which was another commonly available gas in the Planetary Cloud. The nuclei of carbon and oxygen can be fused together at a temperature of fifty million degrees to form the nucleus of another common element called silicon. This element is found in great abundance on Earth and is the seventh most abundant element in the Universe. When combined chemically with oxygen it forms silica which is a very common rock mineral and makes up nearly all the sand we have on Earth today.

The heavy elements

The process of fusion using elements already formed can continue so that at a temperature approaching five hundred million degrees silicon nuclei can take part in a fusion reaction to form iron nuclei. Iron formed in this way was present in both components of the Binary Sun and further quantities of this element formed after the collapse. Hence the Planetary Cloud was very rich in iron and this, as we have seen, played a crucial role in the formation of the planets.

Production of most of the first twenty six elements of the periodic table of elements can be formed by fusion if the temperatures are high enough. These elements also include nitrogen, sodium, aluminium, sulphur, chlorine and calcium. Elements formed by fusion are the most abundant elements to be found in the Solar System. The presence of all these elements on the Earth today gives us some idea of the tremendous temperatures that were generated when the Binary Sun formed and collapsed.

It is interesting to note that the elements that can be formed by fusion are much more abundant than the heavier elements that were formed by the spallation process. This is because the elements formed in the Planetary Cloud by the spallation process were formed in a hit or miss random way.

This being the case the nuclei of heavier elements that required many neutron/proton captures formed less readily than the nuclei of lighter elements that only needed a few neutron/proton captures. For this reason there is a direct correlation between element abundances and atomic numbers so that the heavier an element is the more rare it becomes.

Thus gold with an atomic number of 79 is much rarer than iron with an atomic number of 26. This is because the nucleus of a gold atom has to grow very gradually by the capture of 79 protons one at a time whereas the nucleus of an iron atom is obtained by simply fusing two silicon nuclei.

The well established relationship between element abundances and atomic number supports the theory outlined above that the elements lighter than iron were made readily by the fusion process but the elements heavier than iron were made by a random method requiring an existing exposed nuclei to be hit several times by neutrons/protons while moving about rapidly in the Planetary Cloud.

Element and mineral concentrations

The fusion and spallation methods both produced atom size specks of all elements all randomly mixed with one another in the early turbulence of the Planetary Cloud.

As the Cloud cooled and contracted it became less turbulent and in time the nuclei of various elements were able to regain their electrons and start to make chemical combinations in the normal way with other elements. Elements having a natural affinity for each other were buffeted and moved about within the Cloud until they collided with suitable partners and chemically combined with them.

In this way atoms of all the elements and molecules of millions of different substances were able to form.

The whole Planetary Cloud thus became a huge chemical works in which combinations of all possible types were formed throughout the Cloud.

For example freshly made oxygen was able to easily combine with the previously made abundant hydrogen to form even more molecules of water. The Cloud thus became very rich with water molecules. This is also an important point when we considered how the Earth got its vast oceans of water.

Silicon was also able to react with oxygen to form the very common rock mineral called silica. The Cloud thus contained thousands of billions of tonnes of dust made up from minute specks of this and hundreds of different kinds of common minerals.

Another element chlorine was able to react with sodium to form sodium chloride or common salt which is abundantly present dissolved in our oceans and in other forms. Common gases like ammonia, methane and carbon dioxide and several hydrocarbons were also formed from the available elements when temperature conditions permitted this to happen.

Chemical combinations involving several elements and simpler compounds also became possible, so vast quantities of very complex chemical compounds called clay minerals were also formed as specks of dust randomly scattered throughout the Cloud.

At first all the elements and their compounds including the hundreds of different minerals were still fairly randomly mixed up in the Cloud and as such quite unsuitable for making a planet like the Earth. But Nature had built into the Cloud a mechanism for sorting out these elements and minerals. Tiny specks of different minerals having more or less the same mass were able to form into useful concentrations. Just how this was done was explained in chapter five.

Further Reading
Gill R Chemical Fundamentals of Geology Unwin Hyman London 1989

APPENDIX FIVE

INSIDE THE SUN

'.. made the great lights.. the sun to govern the day..'
(Ps. 136:7)

From dormant body to brilliant star

While the planets were being formed the dormant Sun remained a hardly noticeable dark small but dense body whose only function was to keep all the planets in their orbits and to be a receptacle for unwanted debris in the Planetary Disc of which there was still plenty.

But under its darkened surface a wonderful dynamic system was at work. The two cores (those of Solar A and Solar B) of tightly packed neutrons and iron with a thick shell of frozen hydrogen and helium over each were still rotating rapidly about each other very rapidly and rotating about their own axis all within a medium of extremely dense helium and hydrogen gas and dust. The result of these rotations in a gaseous medium was the generation of enormous heat by friction and some of this heat was used up in the separation of electrons, protons and neutrons from the material of the surrounding medium. These particles thus had the energy to produce the extremely strong Solar Wind - the same wind that helped to scatter and sort the debris from the collapse of the Binary Sun.

In the initial stage the Solar Wind was, as expected, much stronger than it is today. Hence immense quantities of hydrogen and helium that the original components of the Binary Sun had between them were blown away into the very outermost parts of the Solar system billions of kilometres away and well beyond the present orbit of Pluto. Some of this hydrogen and helium is still there in the form of ices which have aggregated into immensely large asteroids. From time to time these work their way back towards their point of origin and can be seen comets in their spiralling orbits inwards to the Sun. We had more to say on this huge reservoir of potential comets earlier on in this book.

While the planets were being formed the Sun continued to produce the Solar Wind but at the same time it was there to reclaim its lost mass and was thus subjected to intense and violent bombardment by giant asteroids and huge quantities of dust. Because of the intense Solar Wind the more volatile material within a colliding body was promptly blown away leaving behind only particles that were too heavy to be affected by the Solar Wind. These particles settled uncomfortably somewhere within the dense hydrogen/helium medium and eventually formed a thick shell thus acting like a protective shield which reduced the intensity of the Solar Wind. The reader will recall that there had to be a reduction in intensity of the Solar Wind from its initial state otherwise the Planetary Disc would not have been able to contract and no planets would have formed. Also the heat generated by friction had to decrease in time as the rotating bodies generating this heat had to slow down in time.

Hence the dormant Sun remained a relatively small but extremely heavy and dark object that would not have been visible from the Earth with the naked eye.

It might have stayed in this darkened state for ever had it not been for another very dramatic event. The only record of this very dramatic event is summed up in just a few words in Genesis. According to the Genesis account a mysterious light floodlit half the Earth for about three days and it is possible to use Biblical chronology to pinpoint this event to 4004 B.C.

'Let there be light. And there was light' (Gen. 1:1)

This was not the light from the Sun but was a precursor of the light to come because according to the same account the

Sun as we know it today only became visible three days after this very strange light had appeared.

Several explanations for this light have been suggested. Some people believe it was a giant comet, others think it was a burst of incandescent gas from a massive volcanic explosion on the Earth and others say that the Solar Wind caused a spectacular aurora (borealis or australis) which is observed in the northern or southern hemisphere when the Solar Wind strikes atoms in the Earth's upper atmosphere causing the gases to glow. Yet others say that it was a miraculous supernatural light, for which no scientific explanation is either necessary or possible and probably an allegorical reference to the life that came upon this dark world, was seen but not understood, and had to die and rise again after three days.

However we can give an explanation that is scientific and in accordance with the story of the creation of the Solar System that has been described so far.

The explanation that can be given here is that the light was indeed from a gigantic comet - so large in size that we can hardly call it a comet as it was more like a small star than a comet. The name Solar C will be used henceforward for this object.

The birth of Solar C

Free neutrons in great abundance were also produced in the great heat generated after the Binary Sun collapsed. There is only a slight difference in mass between an atom of hydrogen and a free neutron so both of these were available in great abundance in the outermost rings of the Planetary Disc. Normally free neutrons do not exist for more than a few minutes and disintegrate into electrons and protons but we can assume that in the outermost regions of the Solar System the temperature was so low that neutrons survived longer by clumping together rather quickly. Neutrons are particles which are magnetic and being magnetic they easily attract one another

213

and form bigger magnets and so on. Hence in only a short while a large number of highly compact and highly magnetic cores of neutrons had formed. Many of these cores then spiralled inwards in the Planetary Disc picking up large quantities of frozen hydrogen and helium in the process. Some of these cores eventually formed asteroids, comets or planets as we have already described but one core in particular was a late developer. This core took its time to gather neutrons from a somewhat dwindled supply and acquired a very rapid rotation by virtue of the angular momentum of the particles from which it had gathered.

With the availability in this region of an abundance of light hydrogen and helium atoms, the now very massive neutron core had no difficulty in attracting these frozen elements to it. As it did so the core grew in size steadily and in this way an extremely large planet probably about fifty or sixty times the size of Jupiter was formed in the outer most regions of the Solar System.

Solar C increased in mass all the time and was unable to hold on to a stable orbit. Being formed in the very outermost regions of the Solar System it had a very long way to go on its spiralling journey inwards towards the dormant Sun and not surprisingly by the time it got near the Sun all the other planets had been completed and had more or less settled in their final orbits.

Solar C completed the final stage of its long journey only about six thousand years ago and invaded the space of the Solar System now occupied by the inner planets. In this final stage its velocity had increased to over a million kilometres per hour.

Travelling at such a high velocity Solar C encountered a great deal of resistance once it entered the still dusty and gas laden inner regions of the Solar System. Being so massive it mopped up everything in its path and doing so its outer layers became heated up. When quite close to the Earth Solar C gained so much heat by the continuous and rapid accretion of debris that its thick atmosphere began to glow like a gigantic comet.

As it approached the still dormant Sun and entered into the dense gases that stretched for millions of kilometres around, it encountered the full intensity of the Solar Wind and its outer layers of gas became even brighter and hotter.

The approach velocity was now so great that this, together with the strong Solar Wind, was able to entirely blow off the glowing atmosphere from the cold dark body under this. We see a similar effect on quite small comets whose tails may be regarded as blown off atmospheres. An observer on Earth at the time would have seen this blown off atmosphere as a huge slow moving rugby shaped ball of light which was strong enough to light up half the surface of the watery Earth.

But the dark and very heavy neutron core with its thick covering of frozen and liquid hydrogen was able to continue its journey towards the dormant Sun. There was thus a separation of the lighted glowing atmosphere from its dark heavy core and the Genesis verse

'.. the light was separated from the darkness.. (Gen. 1.2)

seems to suggest that this is what happened.

The still rapidly rotating core of Solar C, together with its huge quantity of liquid and frozen hydrogen and helium accelerated towards the dormant and darkened Sun and reached its destination about three days after it had lost its outer atmosphere.

When it neared its final destination Solar C encircled the dormant Sun once or twice at tremendous velocity and then like all similar encounters between binary systems it plunged deep into the thick extremely dense layer of hydrogen gas and dust that surrounded the neutron cores of Solar A and Solar B.

The collision when it came resulted as expected in a sudden and huge increase in temperature. Some of the immense kinetic energy that Solar C had was converted to heat and some of the

215

gases and dust in the outer layers of both bodies became white hot. This caused a sudden and huge expansion of already warm gases in the dormant Sun so that within only a few hours the dormant Sun grew in size from a dark tightly compact body of only a few tens of thousands of kilometres in diameter to an immense brilliant and white hot sphere of gas and dust nearly one and a half million kilometres in diameter.

And what only a few days earlier was a dark body suddenly became the brilliant bright star that we depend on utterly for our life on Earth.

What we can see on our Sun now is only this extremely hot and expanded outer layer of gas and dust and on a fine sunny day we have to think of the warmth and light from the Sun as a gift for a limited period only, because it will not last longer than another thousand years.

The nearest star

The Sun is the nearest star to us and affords a splendid opportunity for us to learn something not only about this very special star, but also about the other stars in the Universe. There are many theories about the structure of the Sun and why it functions in the way it does.

The current widely accepted theory is that the Sun is a giant ball of hydrogen with a density that varies from 150 times the density of water at the centre to less than a millionth of this amount in the photosphere. The source of the Sun's heat is believed to be a thermonuclear reaction involving fusion of hydrogen into helium which is said to have begun billions of years ago when the temperature of the core reached about ten million degrees as a result of gravitational compression only. According to this theory the heat generated at the core takes about a million years to reach the photosphere and there is sufficient hydrogen in the sun to keep the process going for another few billion years.

The theory for the Sun that is proposed in this book has already been briefly explained but any theory for the Sun must explain all the important facts about the Sun that we can be fairly certain about. These facts are as follows.

Fact 1 The Photosphere

The part of the Sun that we can see (through very dark filters) is a sphere of blindingly brilliant light called the photosphere. The thickness of this sphere is unknown but we know that it has a diameter of 1.4 million kilometres which is about four times the distance between the Earth and the Moon!

In consistency the photosphere may be described as the surface of an encrusted boiling syrup. This 'crust' is cracked into billions of pieces and each piece is several thousands of square kilometres in area. Hot seething gases escape continuously from the 'cracks' in the 'crust'. The structure of the photosphere is such that astronomers say that it is 'granulated'.

The photosphere may be regarded as the outer 'skin' of the Sun. The gases above the photosphere are mainly hydrogen and helium but appreciable quantities of iron, calcium and other elements can also be detected.

Fact 2 The mass of the Sun

The mass of the Sun is about 330,000 times the mass of the Earth.

Fact 3 Rate of energy output

The rate of heat and light production by the Sun remains remarkably constant. The temperature of the photosphere is only 5800 degrees and does not vary.

Fact 4 Sunspots

Sun Spots which are huge dark blemishes on the photosphere of the Sun, appear near the Sun's equator and vary cyclically in intensity. After reaching a maximum intensity sun spot activity

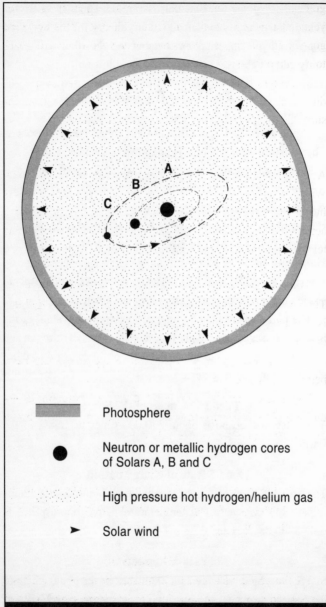

Photosphere

Neutron or metallic hydrogen cores
of Solars A, B and C

High pressure hot hydrogen/helium gas

Solar wind

Inside the Sun

Fig. A5.1

gradually declines and steadily increases again until eleven years later there is another maximum intensity. This cycle has gone on for as long as records have been kept which dates back to over two thousand years.

The spots often occur in pairs that are magnetised in opposite directions and are on average some 20% cooler than the surrounding photosphere.

Fact 5 The Solar Wind

A powerful stream of electrons and protons, called the Solar Wind, radiates from the Sun continuously but this intensity increases in the area of the spots. For this reason sun spot activity is associated with an interference of radio and television communications on the Earth.

Fact 6 Oscillations and rotation of the photosphere

The photosphere appears to breathe like an enormous ball that is inflated and deflated slightly and the period of this oscillation is about five minutes.

Superimposed on this oscillation is another one which has a period of just under an hour.

The photosphere rotates but the rate of rotation is not uniform. At the equator the rate is once every 25 days but at the poles the rate is once every 30 days.

Fact 7 Magnetic field

The Sun has a magnetic field comparable in intensity to the Earth's magnetic field but within the sunspots the intensity is thousands of times greater.

The three in one Sun

All the above facts can be explained in terms of what we have stated so far about how the Sun was formed and some of these can be considered in some detail.

According to the scenario for the formation of the Solar System that we have already described the Sun was once a binary system consisting of two bodies each with rapidly rotating neutron core covered over mainly with frozen, liquid and gaseous hydrogen and helium and other elements in tiny amounts. We have called the two bodies of this binary system Solar A and Solar B.

This binary system subsequently collapsed to form the planets as described in the previous chapters.

After the collapse the cores of the two components continued to rotate very rapidly about each other and around their own axis within a very dense but highly fluidized medium all hidden under a thick atmosphere of gas and dust. The immense heat generated by friction between the rapidly rotating cores and the surrounding extremely dense medium produced the powerful Solar Wind.

At a later stage the dormant sun was hit by Solar C which also had an extremely heavy and rapidly rotating core.

Hence according to our theory the Sun is today made up of the following main components

> The rapidly rotating neutron cores of Solar A, Solar B and Solar C

> A huge reservoir of helium and hydrogen which is extremely dense near the cores but decreases in density further away

> A shell of unknown refractory material.

To understand why the Sun behaves in the way it does we need to consider the part played by each of these components. A drawing of the Sun's interior based on these ideas is shown in Figure A5.1.

When Solar C plunged into the dormant sun the generation of heat was immense. Gas and dust was heated to incandescence and the heat was sufficient to form another nebula, but because of the strong gravitational attraction this nebula became spherical almost immediately and still retains this shape.

The intense Solar Wind and the pressure of hydrogen and helium was able to lift the thick layer of dust to a level where we find it today and recognise it as the photosphere. Above and below the photosphere there is hydrogen and helium.

Below the photosphere the hydrogen and helium is still extremely hot and now acts like a heating element.

The 'element' is heated by the heat generated by friction due the rotations of the cores of Solar A, Solar B and Solar C, which only has to supply sufficient heat to balance the heat lost into space. At times the extremely hot gas that heats up the photosphere is able to break through the photosphere in the form of huge Solar prominences.

The core of Solar A lies close to the core of Solar B and the two rotate together once every 54 minutes.

The smaller core of Solar C rotates in a highly elliptical orbit round the other two cores and moves about slowly in a medium of dense hydrogen and helium gas.

Once every eleven years Solar C comes very close to the photosphere. An elliptical orbit for Solar C is as expected bearing in mind that the core of Solar C is still spiralling its way to the gravitational centre of the sun.

All three cores have retained their original magnetism.

The extremely strong 'wind' called the Solar wind made up of protons, neutrons and electrons radiates away from each of the three cores and this 'wind' pressure holds up the photosphere.

With this model of the Sun we can now proceed to explain most of known features of our Sun.

Why the Sun shines

There was a time when people believed that the Sun was made from burning coal or some other fuel but this idea had to be rejected when simple calculations showed that it could not have lasted more than a few thousand years.

A German scientist Helmholtz suggested that the Sun produced heat because it was shrinking and this could certainly make the Sun last for a few million years.

The current theory is that the sun is a huge nuclear reactor producing energy by turning hydrogen into helium. In this conversion there is a loss of mass which scientists say has been converted into energy. This theory sounds plausible but does not explain all the features of the Sun. Nuclear reactors need to be carefully controlled otherwise a Chernobyl type explosion becomes possible and if this happened on our Sun the entire Solar System would be affected. But no theory as to how the reaction is controlled in the sun has been proposed. Hence the idea that the sun gets its heat from a nuclear reaction can be dismissed.

The theory advanced here is that an appreciable proportion of the hydrogen and helium now in the Sun was returned there by Solar C and became warmed up during transportation, but became extremely hot as a result of the impact between Solar C and the cores of Solar A and Solar B.

The heat output is maintained almost entirely by friction. The gases around the cores are contracting and becoming hotter and this is a frictional effect. But the ice covered cores of Solar A, Solar B and Solar C are all rotating at great speed and being in contact with dense gases and dust, the amount of heat generated by friction is enormous, which contributes greatly to the heat generated by compression.

The Solar Wind also contributes to the generation of heat in the photosphere. The wind contains huge amounts of electrons and these are obliged to flow through the photosphere and cause a generation of heat in much the same way as a flow of electricity through a filament causes heat and light to be released. Hence we can say that the source of the Sun's continuing heat is essentially frictional but electrical as well.

Sunspots

Dark spots have been noticed on the Sun for centuries. Chinese astronomers were clearly very worried about the very large blemishes on the Sun's surface and may have believed that the end of the Sun and hence the world was imminent. They could do nothing about it except watch the progress of the spots and keep records. The earliest record dates back to 200 B.C.

The spots become worse each year, reaching a maximum intensity, which then decreases to a minimum intensity and so on back to a maximum intensity with an eleven year period between two maximum intensities. The problem was serious enough for Astronomers to keep records of this phenomenon and for this reason we know that ever since these records were kept this eleven year cycle of sunspot activity has been repeated to the present time. Sun spot activity is also restricted only to certain latitudes, meaning that sunspot activity is not a random thing that happens anywhere on the surface, but only in a well defined region and this too has to be explained.

Most textbooks on Astronomy fail to give an explanation for this sunspot cycle. The model for the Sun that we have presented here explains the cyclical nature of sunspot activity quite adequately as follows.

The two cores at the centre of the Sun (Solar A and Solar B) are highly magnetic, as is the core of Solar C which now orbits in a medium of gaseous and liquid hydrogen round the centre of the Sun. Sun spot activity reaches a maximum when Solar C is closest to the photosphere and its magnetic field stretches out to puncture the photosphere, causing a reduction in density of the photosphere. This results in a cooling of the region which

223

manifested in a greater escape of Solar Wind through the 'holes' so created. The temperature at the centre of a sunspot is about 20% lower than the temperature of the rest of the photosphere, and the strength of the magnetic field inside a spot is thousand times stronger than outside the spot. The intensity of the Solar Wind during sunspot activity is often great enough to cause communication problems and atmospheric interference on Earth.

Sun spots appear in oppositely charged pairs suggesting that in one spot the direction of the magnetic force is outwards but in its partner the direction of the force is inwards, which is what we would expect if the magnetic field was caused by something like the very powerfully magnetised neutron core of Solar C. This orbit of the core of Solar C within the Sun explains the cyclical nature of the sunspots, their magnetism and their appearance only within certain latitudes of the Sun.

Oscillation of the photosphere

The photosphere vibrates inwards and outwards by as much as 10 kilometres every fifty-four minutes.

Our model of the Sun explains this oscillation as a manifestation of the residual rotation of the cores of Solar A and Solar B about each other.

Because of this rotation the centre of gravity of the Sun changes slightly during a fifty-four minute cycle and this change is observed in the photosphere which moves inwards when the centre of gravity is nearest and moves outwards when the centre of gravity is further away.

The photosphere also has another oscillation with a period of about five minutes. This is explained as a thermostat to keep the heat output from the Sun constant. If the Sun gets too hot the photosphere expands thus allowing more of the Solar Wind to escape and cool the photosphere in the process. If the temperature drops the photosphere contracts, thus trapping a little more of the Solar Wind and allowing more of it to have a frictional effect and heat the photosphere. Thus the five minute oscillations are a manifestation of the wonderful thermostat control system that our Sun has.

The future of the Sun

The explanation for the Sun given in this chapter is in accordance with the theme of this book. This explanation may be unacceptable to many people because it means that the Sun did not start to shine until very recently and that the Sun will only last for as long as its neutron cores keep on rotating. This may be only a tiny fraction of the life predicted by conventional theory.

One interpretation of the writings about the Sun in the Bible is that the Sun only began to shine about six thousand years ago and that it will cease to shine in about a thousand years from now. There is a prediction in the Bible that the carefully controlled thermostat arrangement will not always work and could break down from time to time

'.. and the sun was given power to scorch people with fire. They were seared by the intense heat... (Rev. 16:8)

'the sun will be turned into darkness..' (Acts 2:20)

Despite these failings the Sun is still a wonderful creation and has been worshiped as a god since time began. But it is not a god and one day people of this Earth will be horrified by its behaviour which for so long they have taken for granted.

Further Reading
Kaufmann W J *Discovering the Universe (Chapter 11)* W H Freeman & Co New York 1990
Robinson L *The Disquieting Sun: How Big, How Steady* Sky & Telescope April 1982

View of Mercury

Fig. A6.1

226

APPENDIX SIX

MERCURY, VENUS AND MARS

' The sun has one kind of splendour, the moon another and the stars another' (1. Cor. 15:41)

A whistle stop tour of the planets

In chapter five we described in general terms how the planets were formed from the dust and asteroids in the Planetary Disc which were impacted layer by layer on a foundation core of iron or a combination of iron and other magnetic material.

In this Appendix and the next two we consider each planet in turn and look at some of the well known features about them and explain how these features are consistent with the theory for their formation that we have outlined.

This book is essentially about the creation of our own planet Earth and not about the other planets. But all the other planets are different and equally wonderful in their own way and were formed at the same time from the same Planetary Cloud. Each of these planets and their moons also tells us something about the early history of our own planet and for this reason it is useful and logical to examine each of the other planets and their satellites.

In the this and the next two appendices we take a journey across the Solar System and hop from planet to planet, starting with Mercury, which is the planet nearest the Sun, and work our way outwards from there to the remotest planet (as far as we know) Pluto.

Mercury

The construction of Mercury started with a few particles of iron which then aggregated with more particles until a solid iron core was formed as described in chapter five. This core was probably formed somewhere in the Inner Region of the Planetary Disc and was thus able to attract material from the rings of material and asteroids in this region which contained high density material. In this way Mercury built up a mantle and crust over its iron core and the planet was completed very quickly.

Its appearance has not changed very much since then and is the same today as it was when it was first formed.

Close up photographs of Mercury show the planet to be fairly uniformly constructed, so that there are no real differences between the northern and southern hemisphere, and from this we can conclude that Mercury was formed as a single planet layer by layer by a uniformly distributed collection of asteroids and dust.

As Mercury consists of an iron core and heavier dust particles from the Planetary Disc, it should have the highest density of all planets. Observations and calculations confirm that this is the case.

Mercury did not receive any gases and ices from the Outer Regions because Mercury is a small planet having only 1/20 of the mass of the Earth and was much too close to the Sun, and thus beyond the reach of even the very heavy gases of the Outer Region.

Any gases it might have gained would in any case have been driven off by the fierce ever present Solar Wind, which is of much greater intensity on Mercury than it is on Earth.

Mercury has no moons and rotates only once in every about 60 days.It has a year of 88 days which means it takes just under three months for the planet to complete one orbit round the Sun.

Daytime on this planet lasts about a month because of its very slow rate of rotation. Mercury's rotation is slow because its iron core did not have far to travel and hence did not pick up much angular momentum. Nevertheless its rotation about its own axis is still faster than it should be. Being so close to the

Sun it should slow down so that it will take as long to revolve round its axis as it does to go round the Sun once, so that only one side will be in permanent daytime and the other will remain in permanent darkness. This is what has happened to the rotation of the Moon around the Earth and is the reason why only one face of the Moon is visible from the Earth. The fact that this has not as yet happened with Mercury and the Sun implies that Mercury is a very young planet that still enjoys some of the rotation it derived from the asteroids and dust of the Planetary Disc.

Mercury has no water on its surface but may have water below its surface. Because of its close proximity to the Sun and low gravitational attraction any water that might have been picked up or squeezed out from its interior would have been evaporated and driven off quickly.

This lack of water or dense atmosphere on Mercury is helpful in our understanding of all the planets. In Mercury we have a truly bare planet which enables us to appreciate what our own planet must have looked like immediately after it had collected its quota of dust and asteroids from the Inner Region but before it became clothed with air and water from the Outer Region of the Planetary Disc.

Mercury's surface, like our Moon, is pock marked with impact craters. The photographs taken of it by Mariner 10 in 1974 show the numerous impact craters very clearly and this enables us to estimate the number and approximate size of the asteroids that were involved in the belt of asteroids which contributed to the last stages of its construction.

The presence of these impact craters supports the theory that we have outlined in previous chapters that each planet was formed by small and large asteroids of cold, previously sorted out rock material.

Mercury has a magnetic field that is weaker than the Earth's. The origin of a planets magnetic field is still a subject of some debate but according to the theory for the Solar System outlined in this book, the strength of a planet's magnetic field depends on the size of its core and Mercury started off as a small core. The fact that Mercury's magnetism has not quite gone suggests that this planet is a young planet, as magnetism on our own planet is decreasing very rapidly and the same must be true for other planets.

The only atmosphere now present on this planet is a very small amount of helium and this is easily explained. Mercury was formed mainly from heavy dust particles but there was also an abundance of helium in the rings of the Planetary Disc at the same time. This helium thus became trapped in the interior of the planet and is now steadily seeping out. During its long night time when this part of the planet is sheltered from the Solar Wind the amount of helium that accumulates becomes detectable.

In conclusion it may be said that as far as we can tell there is no feature about the planet Mercury which is not in accordance with the theory for the Solar System that has been outlined in this book.

Venus

Venus was formed in a little more complicated and interesting way than Mercury, because Venus is another example of a binary collapse involving two smaller planets.

Both of these small planets began by the formation of an iron core which spiralled through the Planetary Disc and gathered up asteroids and dust as the other planets did.

Initially both of these would have looked like Mercury with its bare crater marked surface, but one planet was significantly larger than the other. For a while both planets enjoyed independent existences on separate adjacent orbits although they came dangerously close to each other on several occasions.

When the Planetary Disc contracted further both planets found gases of the Outer Regions.

The two semi-planets began to increase in mass very slightly as they swept up the dust and gases from the rings of these regions. This included heavy gases like carbon dioxide, chlorine and sulphur trioxide in the form of small icy particles. In the intense cold both planets were able to pick up sufficient material to form a thick ice layer on their surfaces.

Although quite small this additional mass on the two components however was sufficient to tip the balance. At their next close encounter the gravitational attraction was just too much and the two planets captured each other and formed a binary planet for a while.

This was an unstable binary and both components began to spiral inwards towards each other. Eventually the smaller of the two effectively wrapped itself round the larger, disintegrated and vaporised on impact creating a huge rotating cloud of hot gas and dust. For a while this cloud stretched for thousands of kilometres around the now single planet but then contracted rapidly as a result of the strong gravitational pull of the now combined planets.

This cloud is still present round the planet today. This is why the surface of Venus has been hidden from view from the Earth until very recently. The cloud was originally much bigger and hotter than it is today but has now cooled and contracted and all that remains of it is a thick fog made up of tiny droplets of liquid. The chemistry of this liquid is uncertain but is believed to contain sulphuric acid. If this is correct it would be in accordance with the theory that we have outlined because the gases contained in the rings would have included such heavy gases as sulphur trioxide and water vapour which combine to form sulphuric acid.

The cloud is still very thick and Astronomers have only been able to study the planet's surface by penetrating the cloud by radar and soft landings of space probes.

The great thickness of the cloud has prevented light from the Sun penetrating through, although the Sun's rays on Venus are very much more powerful there than they are on Earth. Hence Venus remains a dimly lit planet and the only source of bright light is the extremely frequent bouts of lightening caused by the discharge of static electricity as the rapidly rotating cloud becomes charged by the powerful Solar Wind, and when this becomes too great a gigantic flash of lightening occurs.

The cloud also forms a thick insulating layer round the planet, which prevents heat from the planet from escaping into space. For this reason much of the heat generated in the binary collapse is still trapped at the surface. The temperature on the surface of the planet is now several hundred degrees, which is more than sufficient not only to melt all the frozen material at the surface, but high enough to melt soft metals such as lead. This high temperature prevents the cloud from cooling and condensing quickly, and thus clearing the view.

As expected the cloud revolves rapidly round the planet. Its estimated speed is in excess of 1000km per hour so that it takes just over a hundred hours to complete one revolution round the planet. This contrasts with the rotation of the planet itself which is almost at a standstill but does in fact rotate so slowly that the time from dawn to dusk on a Venusian day is about four months. On Venus the Sun rises in the West and sets in the East. This somewhat inconsistent rotation is due to the friction that was generated when the two planets came together. This can easily be demonstrated by considering two rubber balls in contact with each other. If one ball is rotated in a clockwise direction then the other, if in touch, will be forced to rotate in an anticlockwise direction and something like this happened when the two planets came together.

It is clear from this that the rotation of the cloud is not as yet linked with the rotation of the planet itself, and when it does we may have a rotation of this planet which is consistent with the rotations of the other planets. The rotation of the core of Venus is not known but it is quite possible that the outer layers of Venus rotate independently of its core.

Photographs taken by soft landing craft on Venus by Soviet scientists suggest that the surface is strewn with sharp edged and angular rocks, suggesting that there has been no erosion to smooth out the edges. Measurements of wind speed at the surface show only gentle breezes and confirm that the fast moving cloud is well above the surface.

As expected for the rapidly rotating cloud its thickness is less at the poles than it is at the equator, and this suggests that the cloud is beginning to flatten into a disc. The fact that this has not as yet happened may be taken as a sign of the relative youth of the cloud.

The cloud already shows signs of banding into layers and may eventually flatten into a disc, which would then split into rings, form a belt of asteroids, and finally into small satellites. The cloud may therefore be taken as a miniature model of the Planetary Cloud formed when the Binary Sun collapsed.

Below the swirling Cloud Venus has a dense atmosphere. This is mainly composed of carbon dioxide with very small amounts of carbon monoxide, hydrochloric acid and argon. Venus gained its atmosphere of carbon dioxide by finding itself orbiting those regions of the Planetary Disc which were rich in the heavy and abundantly available gases such as carbon dioxide and sulphur trioxide.

Because of the covering that the Cloud provides, no optical photographs of the planets surface taken from the Earth are available. Radar waves bounced off the planet show mountain chains, long deep valleys, large volcanoes and impact craters. The presence of deep valleys and mountain chains on Venus is interesting. One such crack in its southern hemisphere is 4000km long, 240km wide and 65m deep. This long and deep valley is very probably the result of the damage done to the surface shell when its binary companion collided. Here on Earth there are similar features.

The mountain chains can also be explained as a consequence of the impact of its binary companion. This explanation is also discussed in this book with reference to the formation of the many mountain chains on Earth.

The large volcanoes are a manifestation of the tremendous heat generated by the impact, and impact craters found on Venus are the result of late arrival asteroids from the belts of asteroids from which the planet was formed.

From these observations we conclude that there are reasonable grounds for believing that Venus was once a close binary planet and that its two components have come together fairly recently.

Mars

The planet Mars is our other immediate neighbour. Whereas Venus lies closer to the Sun than the Earth, Mars lies on the other side further away from the Earth. Being so close to us it is a planet for which we have thousands of detailed photographs and measurements taken by the Mariner and Viking space probes in the seventies.

Mars also began its existence as two semi-planets.

Each semi-planet began as an iron core revolving around the darkened dormant Sun in slightly different orbits.

Both cores then became covered over with asteroids and dust from the Disc and became independent semi-planets for a while.

Each of the semi-planets continued to orbit the dormant Sun for a while until the Planetary Disc contracted further. Thus both semi-planets were able to pick up some of the frozen ices and gases from the Disc and became covered by a thick layer of hailstones of water and frozen carbon dioxide. A photograph of

234

the semi planets at this stage would have shown two giant snowballs.

The orbits taken by each semi-planet were sufficiently different so that the proportion of carbon dioxide and water vapour acquired by each semi-planet was different. Thus one semi-planet picked up mainly frozen carbon dioxide with some water vapour and the other picked up mainly water vapour but with some carbon dioxide. Because of their increase in mass both components could no longer enjoy independent orbits and became increasingly attracted to one another and with each revolution they grew closer to each other. Finally the two semi-planets joined up relatively gently (the relative velocity between then was very low) to form the single planet Mars as we know it today.

This scenario for the formation of Mars forms a reasonable explanation for all the physical features of Mars as we find them today. A few features of the planet illustrates this.

In terms of density Mars should have a density that is less than that of Mercury, Venus and Earth because all these three planets derived their planet making material from high density particles of the Planetary Disc, whereas Mars derived its material from the medium and low density particles of the Disc.

Observations and calculations show that the average density of Mars is as expected and in accordance with its mode of formation as described.

Mars has a very light atmosphere consisting of carbon dioxide, nitrogen, argon and some oxygen. This atmosphere is again as expected because these gases together with water vapour were present in the regions in which Mars found itself in orbit.

Mars therefore, has as expected, much water but because of the very low temperature of the planet all this water is frozen.

Today this water is hidden from view because it lies below the surface as a shell of subterranean ice which became covered over by other material from the Planetary Disc. Showers of sand and asteroids from the rings of the Planetary Disc covered the planet well after it had obtained its water.

The tremendous amount of sand has now been wind driven into huge dunes which are found throughout the planet. The exposed part of the subterranean ice shell now only accounts for about 10% of the entire surface of Mars.

At the time of the collision of the semi-planets some of this ice melted and vast quantities of water were produced that caused extensive flooding with all the geological consequences of such a flood. Erosional features on the planet's surface are quite common and it is clear that the Martian surface has been shaped to a certain extent by these flood waters. These waters were, however, produced very quickly by melting and because of the very low atmospheric pressure on Mars all the melted water either evaporated very quickly or froze up again. For this reason no free water is found on the planet today.

The existence of ice under the superficial layer of sand on Mars is an important and relevant feature to the Earth's formation because a very similar situation also existed (and may still exist) on the Earth as well.

Mars is slightly pear shaped - the sort of shape that is formed by joining together two spheres of different diameters. Remote from the collision site the frozen gases are still present at the surface, so that the Southern Pole is made up of frozen water ice and the Northern Pole made up from frozen carbon dioxide.

The two hemispheres of Mars also show an age difference. The northern hemisphere is hotter than the southern hemisphere so that volcanoes in abundance are found in the northern hemisphere. In the southern hemisphere the surface has fewer volcanoes but many impact craters.

The two hemispheres are separated by a vast canyon called

the Valles Marineris which is some 4000km long, upto 20km wide and nearly 6000m deep. It would seem that the join has not yet closed up!

Another striking feature on Mars, which is also relevant to our planet, is the Tharsis Shield. This is a dome-shaped swelling which is a like huge blister which has been forced to swell above the normal surface of the planet. A possible explanation for this swelling is that it is the location of the first 'kiss' from its companion before the two became one. Such a large pressure dome is a feature found on the Earth as well but is covered over with the waters of the Pacific Ocean.

The formation of a 'blister' is the result of an increase in temperature which causes an increase in internal pressures as well as a weakening of the crust. Within the Tharsis Shield dome this pressure has been partly relieved by the formation of numerous volcanoes. Possibly the biggest volcano in the Solar System is found in this area. It is the volcano Olympus Mons which measures 600km across at its base and rises 21km above the surface. This is more than twice the height of the highest submarine mountains on Earth (Mauna Loa in Hawaii and Mount Teide in the Canary Islands) and more than twice higher than Mt Everest. Olympus Mons is made from basalt a very common type of rock which is found throughout the Earth in land and ocean beds and on the Moon as well.

A dome such as the Tharsis Shield puts the basaltic crust into tension and hence it is not surprising to find that huge cracks or fractures hundreds of kilometres long and a few hundred metres deep have also appeared. Between any two such fractures the crust has slumped down again as a result of escape of gases including vaporised rock and water. Some of the vast sand deposits on Mars may also be due to condensation of this vaporised rock. Thus we see on Mars another of the mechanisms that have also played a similar part in the shaping of the Earth's surface.

Another interesting and relevant feature of Mars is an impact crater called Arandas. This is unusual in that the surrounding area appears to have been formed by waves of mud which spread outwards and then solidified. The cause of this is said to be the melting of subterranean ice by the impact of an asteroid but an equally plausible explanation is that the offending asteroid may have been made entirely from water and clay minerals, and what we see in the mud waves of Arandas is the remains of this asteroid. A proportion of the vast amounts of clays found on the Earth was probably formed very quickly in this way.

In conclusion we may say that many, if not all, of the features of Mars may be explained by the theory we have postulated and we can with increased confidence apply the same theory to understanding the Earth's formation and its features.

The Asteroid Belt

Between the orbits of the planets Mars and Jupiter lies a collection of asteroids which failed in the past to aggregate into a planet and are unlikely to do so in the future. This particular ordered collection of asteroids is called the Asteroid Belt but there are millions of other asteroids which are not part of the belt and have not as yet settled into an orbit in the same plane as the rest of the planets.

The reason why the asteroids of the Belt will not form into a planet is because the iron core that would have gathered up these asteroids was attracted away by what is called the Jupiter effect. From time to time the combined gravitational attraction of the Sun and Jupiter is such that asteroids from the Belt are knocked off their regular orbits in the Belt and become free to find a resting place on one of the other planets. Some of them end up in one of two other collections of asteroids called the Leading Trojan group and the Trailing Trojan group. These groups of asteroids share the same orbit and the same velocity around the Sun as Jupiter but are either exactly 60 degrees ahead or 60 degrees behind Jupiter. The fact that not all the asteroids have been captured in this way by Jupiter is also indicative of the relative youth of the Solar System.

Asteroids are large chunks of rock, iron or ice and combinations of these in various shapes which may be anything from a few metres long to hundreds of kilometres in diameter. They may be regarded as the bricks from which all the planets have been built up. As the Solar System is young the building process has still not been completed and it is not surprising to find the Solar System littered with them, as one would expect with bricks on a building site where work is still continuing. Thousands of these asteroids have been named and plotted but possibly millions more await to be fully and formally identified. If a computer analysis of the orbits of all the asteroids could be carried out we would be able to find that when our planet Earth would next be hit by an asteroid of some size.

We can quote three examples of fairly recent near misses that have been recorded but there were undoubtedly many more that went unrecorded.

In 1937 asteroid Hermes was less than a million kilometres from us. In 1968 asteroid Icarus was six million kilometres away and in 1989 a previously unidentified asteroid (now called asteroid 1989FC) came only within a few hundred thousand kilometres from us. With vastly improved telescopes and computational facilities we should be able to predict future near misses or collisions with greater accuracy, but if an astronomer is able to discover a large asteroid which will be on collision course with the Earth, the chances are that his discovery will be kept secret for fear of causing panic in populations likely to be affected.

The average density of asteroid Ceres, which belongs to the belt has been estimated and found to be 2.3, which is as expected smaller than that of Mars (5.5) but larger than that of

Belt were formed from the dust in the Planetary Disc, which was not as heavy as the dust from which Mars was formed, but heavier than the dust and gas from which Jupiter was formed.

The string of asteroids that hit the Planet Jupiter recently was carefully monitored by astronomers all over the world and in particular by the Hubble space telescope. This string of 21 asteroids was discovered by concentrating a search in one region of space called the Jupiter field. It was named Shoemaker Levy 9 after its discoverers. The observational and computational skills of the discoverers and their team was illustrated dramatically when the time and location of the impact of each asteroid in the collection was recorded exactly as predicted.

The existence of such a string is easily explained as the asteroids formerly in one of the many rings of the Planetary Disc. Our own planet Earth still receives a great deal of dust and small meteors. It has been estimated that some 300 tons of extraterrestrial material is added to the Earth's mass each day. A large number of the meteorites have been collected from the Earth's surface and studied, and it is clear from this study that our planet still regularly receives samples of asteroid material which are either wholly made of iron (iron core material) or a mixture of iron and rock (very heavy matter material) or wholly made of rock (medium heavy matter). Numerous asteroids made wholly from ice have also hit the Earth but because these evaporate before they are found and only a very few cases have been recorded.

In conclusion to this short discussion on the asteroids we can say that the existence and nature of the asteroids fits in with the theory that we have proposed for the formation of the Solar

Further Reading
Kaufmann W J *Discovering the Universe (Chapter 7)*
W H Freeman & Co New York 1990

APPENDIX SEVEN

JUPITER

'The light shines in the darkness, but the darkness has not understood it' (John 1:5)

The Missing Planet X

In the previous Appendix we considered the three terrestrial planets which are relatively near the Sun and made up essentially of heavy rocky material. This Appendix is devoted only to the giant planet Jupiter because it has some interesting features that are relevant to the manner in which the Earth was created.

Jupiter and its many moons may be regarded as a mini solar system because Jupiter was once a binary system which collapsed and the consequence of this collapse was the formation of moons and rings, in much the same way as when the Binary Sun collapsed to form the planets. The only difference between the formation of the planets and the formation of Jupiter's moons is one of scale.

Jupiter's binary companion was a smaller planet which we can call Planet X. This planet began like all other planets with the formation of a core of iron in the outer parts of the Planetary Disc. This core quickly grew to an immense size by picking up most of the iron it encountered on its inward spiralling through the Planetary Disc. The core attained a size at which it became so massive that it was able to attract other material from the Disc, and thus obtained a significant amount of light gases and dust as it spiralled its way to somewhere near where the Asteroid Belt now is. At this point it was almost a fully fledged planet with a diameter thought to be four or five times that of the Earth's diameter. It should have swept up the rest of the

241

asteroids in the belt had it been there long enough. But this was not to be. While Planet X was being formed the main planet Jupiter was also being formed. Jupiter itself also began as an iron or neutoron core in the outer regions of the Planetary Disc. When the core grew to a large enough size it had no difficulty attracting large asteroids and gases made up of hydrogen and helium. This core also grew rapidly in size as it spiralled its way inwards in the Planetary Disc to very close to its present orbit.

By the time it had arrived at this position it was able to sweep up an immense amount of hydrogen and helium and at the same time capture the angular momentum of the gas and asteroids it had acquired and thus became a giant planet with a diameter of over 142,000km and heavier than twice all the rest of the planets put together. Most of the collected material was hydrogen, so the planet is made up of a very thick atmosphere of normal hydrogen gas below which is an immense and extremely deep ocean of liquid hydrogen. At a certain depth in this vast ocean the pressure is so great that the hydrogen has turned into a metallic form.

When Jupiter and Planet X were thus formed, the two planets enjoyed a period of independence in their own orbits for a short while. But as there was still plenty of gas and dust to pick up from the Planetary Disc, the masses of the two new planets became critical and on the next close encounter Jupiter was able to attract Planet X to itself and capture it to form a binary system. (Jupiter continues to knock off asteroids from the belt from time to time even today for the same reason)

For a short while Planet X rotated around Jupiter but as both were still increasing steadily in mass, a collapse became inevitable.

As with most binary collapses the collision was not a direct head on one but a glancing one.

In the encounter the outer parts of Planet X disintegrated

before impact. Huge waves of liquid hydrogen were also raised and the outer parts of Planet X became mixed with the atmospheric and oceanic hydrogen and temperatures of millions of degrees attained as the immense kinetic energy of the system became converted to heat energy. Most of Planet X thus became vaporised and the vaporised material immediately formed into a huge expanding cloud.

But not all of Planet X evaporated into a cloud. The core and possibly its covering of a red oxide of iron was able to plunge into the hydrogen ocean and to sink into it to a depth where its downward weight was just balanced by the upward pressure of the liquid hydrogen where it still lies today.

Astronomers were fortunate to see what happens when a large asteroid crashes on to Jupiter when the Shoemaker-Levy series of asteroids plunged into Jupiter recently.

The cloud of dust and gas generated by the binary collapse can be compared to the planetary nebula cloud which was formed when the Binary Sun collapsed.

The dust/gas cloud behaved in a very similar way to the much bigger Planetary Cloud and hence in the collapse of the Jupiter Binary we have a repeat performance on a much smaller scale of the formation of the Solar System.

The cloud retained much of the original angular momentum of Planet X and hence quickly engulfed Jupiter and rotated about it and flattened into a disc as it rotated around Jupiter's equator. In time this disc also split up into rings. Each ring contained dust particles which were sorted out according to their mass under a combination of gravitational and centrifugal forces.

Because of the very large magnetic field that Jupiter has, it is probable that the first particles to aggregate within the rings were magnetic ones and these then formed the nuclei for further particles to aggregate on to.

Some of these rings are still faintly discernible near the planet but most of the other rings have now gone into the formation of the many moons of Jupiter in exactly the same way as the material of the Planetary Disc went on to form planets.

With this brief history of the formation of Jupiter and its moons we can proceed now to consider the features of the planet and show how they relate to the formation of our own planet Earth.

Jupiter as a small dormant star

Jupiter has an average density of 1.3 which is only 30% greater than the density of water. Jupiter's density is as expected. The density is smaller than that of the density of its neighbour Mars which is closer to the Sun.

This supports our theory that Mars was formed as explained from a ring of heavier material in the Solar Nebula Cloud whereas Jupiter was built up from much lighter material.

Jupiter's density is, as expected, also larger than that of its other neighbour Saturn which is further away from the Sun. Thus we can conclude that the average densities of the planets Mars, Jupiter and Saturn would tend to support the theory that the Planetary Disc sorted itself out according to the atomic and molecular masses as described in Chapter 5.

The actual composition of Jupiter has been worked out and is thought to be 80% hydrogen 19% helium and 1% other material.

This is more or less the same composition as the Sun is today, so we now have in Jupiter an example of what a smaller version of the dormant Sun may have looked like.

Jupiter rotates very rapidly about its axis taking only 590 minutes to revolve once at the equator and 596 minutes at the poles. This difference in rotation speeds at the equator and poles arises because what is being measured is the rotation of that part of the dust/gas cloud which became friction bound to the surface of the planet. Below the cloud is the liquid hydrogen ocean of the planet, and the rotation rate of the liquid ocean may be somewhat different from the rotation of the outer clouds.

Planet X should have been where the Asteroid Belt now is and this planet is predicted by the Titus-Bode rule but could not be found and this is because it was captured and destroyed by Jupiter and all that is left of it is its core and the moons of Jupiter.

The Great Red Spot

One of the most intriguing features of Jupiter is a huge red spot which has puzzled astronomers ever since its discovery some four hundred years ago.

The Spot is elliptical in shape being about 40,000km long and 13,000km wide. It is important to get some appreciation of the size of this feature. A modern passenger airliner would take about two days to travel from one end of the spot to the other and all the time a passenger would see the spot stretch from horizon to horizon. It has an area equal to the entire surface area of the Earth and we could easily fit three Earths into it side by side.

Observations from Earth suggest that the spot is not fixed to the surface but moves a little, somewhat irregularly, from side to side like a boat that has been moored and responds to the motion of the water around it. It also rotates round its own axis in an anticlockwise direction once every six days.

The temperature of the Spot is a few degrees lower than that of the surrounding clouds.

It also undergoes a slight change in colour from pink to brick red. Its size and orientation have also varied with time and there has been at least one brief period in history when it disappeared altogether only to reappear. Some Astronomers believe that it has travelled right round the planet.

Other Astronomers have reported that the Spot appears to stick out above the top of the clouds.

The question of what precisely is the Great Red Spot is one that has been asked for centuries and a number of explanations have been put forward. Some Astronomers believe it is a region of high atmospheric pressure, and this may be correct, but we still need a reason for its shape, colour or steadiness of location.

The explanation that we offer for the Spot is consistent with the theory that Jupiter once had a binary companion and, according to the scenario described above, the Great Red Spot marks the location where the intact core of Planet X finally came to rest on Jupiter.

The high atmospheric pressure is due to the localised increase in the surface gravity (called a gravitational anomaly) caused by the proximity of the iron core of Planet X in the hydrogen ocean. The increased gravity also has the effect of pulling down the clouds so that the Spot appears to stick above the clouds.

The red coloration may be due to the way in which the Sun's light penetrates the denser atmosphere but there is also the possibility that the colour is due to the red oxide of iron (hematite) or red phosphorus contained in the core of the submerged Planet X. Thus red iron oxide or red phosphorus in powder form would be expected over a very wide area surrounding the burial site and now forms an immensely large red iceberg floating like a raft on hydrogen liquid.

The apparent movement of the Red Spot is explained by the wind movements around the 'iceberg'. The temperature difference has allowed a cyclic wind pattern to develop and the whirling clouds around the Spot are able to rotate the giant red 'iceberg', and once set in rotation it would do so uniformly like an immensely massive flywheel. It is also probable that the rotation that Planet X had about its own axis just before the submergence has been preserved to a certain extent in its submerged core. We must wait for further close up photographs of Jupiter's surface for this theory to be confirmed, but all the evidence so far would tend to support the theory that the Great Red Spot is simply either a giant red iceberg made from red iron oxide dust and frozen hydrogen which is able to travel round the planet and is able to rock from side to side and is liable to disappear from view from time to time or it may still be a high pressure region caused by the presence of something very massive such as the red core of another planet.

The moons of Jupiter

In Jupiter and its moons we have a Solar System in miniature formed in exactly the same way as the Solar System from a rotating cloud of gas and dust. Jupiter is to its moons what the Sun was (and is) to the planets, and so their study also tells us quite a lot about how our own planet was formed.

Moreover some of the moons give us a clue as to how our planet came to have oceans and continents and how the ice ages came upon our planet quite suddenly.

Jupiter has at least fourteen moons but only the first five are of any real size and these are as follows

Moon	Diameter km	Density water = 1.0	Distance from planet km
Amalthea	160	4.0?	181,300
Io	3640	3.50	421,600
Europa	3060	3.04	670,900
Ganymede	5220	1.94	1,070,800
Callisto	4990	1.81	1,880,000

The first interesting fact to note about the moons is their average density. As expected the density of each of the five moons varies with distance from Jupiter so that the nearest moon Amalthea has a greater density to the next nearest moon Io and so on for Europa, Ganymede and Callisto.

All five of these moons lie in the plane of Jupiter's equator so it is clear from this that the Cloud caused by the impact with Planet X and the single planet Jupiter revolved in unison for a while. While revolving, the Cloud sorted itself out according to the mass of each of its dust particles and flattened into a disc. The disc then split into rings and from each ring one moon was formed. The moons of Jupiter thus display the same density variation as the planets do with respect to their distance from the Sun.

We also know something about the composition of each of the moons. It is apparent that the Cloud underwent some segregation of its dust, so that the heavier dust particles remained nearer the planet than the lighter dust particles and this segregation is now reflected in the composition of each of the moons of Jupiter.

Each of the main moons of Jupiter tells us something different about the way in which our own planet Earth was formed and it is relevant to examine these briefly here. We begin with the moon nearest the planet and work our way upwards to the most distant moon.

Amalthea

The nearest moon Amalthea is only 160km in diameter but quite dense. It has a very red surface and this suggests that this satellite is also made up almost entirely of the oxide of iron called hematite or red phosphorus. This supports the theory that we have outlined for the Great Red Spot because the material that formed Amalthea appears to be of the same colour as the material in the Great Red Spot. It also supports the theory that the moons of Jupiter were formed at about the same time from the same cloud of gas and dust that resulted from the impact of Planet X with Jupiter. Amalthea confirms that this cloud differentiated itself according to density so that the heavy iron rich dust particles lay nearest the surface of Jupiter, flattened into a disc and formed a ring round Jupiter which finally aggregated into a moon.

Amalthea also supports the theory that iron cores of the planets were formed first because this moon may be regarded as a core which is still waiting to be covered over with lighter material.

Amalthea has a density greatly in excess of the density of Jupiter itself. The planet Mercury also has a density that is much greater than the average density of the Sun so Amalthea and Mercury can be compared with each other in terms of density.

Io

The next of Jupiter's moon is Io, which is a little larger than our Moon but is very different. Whereas our Moon is a basaltic grey in colour Io is orangey yellow and has numerous volcanoes all emitting sulphur in prodigious quantities. Sulphur is one of the elements that can be formed in abundance by the fusion process and is next to iron in the order of abundances. It is also lighter than iron, so it is not surprising to find that the moon next to the iron Amalthea has a large proportion of Sulphur.

Another interesting feature of Io is that it orbits within a ring of hydrogen. This hydrogen ring can be regarded as a remnant of the Jupiter Cloud now in ring form, as expected, and is a little illustration of how all the planets of the Solar System obtained their atmospheres by orbiting in rings of gas concentrated with one or two different gases.

Europa

Europa has a density which is less than Io but more than the next moon out, Ganymede. Its surface is completely covered with water ice which is easily explained. Europa gained a mantle of ice when it found itself in orbit in a ring composed entirely of particles of water ice. Water vapour in huge quantities was one of the constituents of the Jupiter/Planet impact cloud, and much of this water was imported and introduced into the cloud by Planet X.

Europa attracted ice particles and thus developed a thick shell of ice. The thickness of this shell is estimated at 100km, which if melted would give more water than is contained in all the oceans of the Earth put together. This is a staggering amount and illustrates the quantity of water that must have been contained as vapour in the Jupiter/Planet X impact cloud.

Europa's thick shell of ice is also very relevant to the understanding of the Earth's formation as we explained in Chapter Six how the Earth was also completely covered over by ice and water.

Europa's ice shell is severely cracked and there is some evidence to suggest that from time to time liquids have seeped out through the cracks and then promptly froze on the surface. The cause of cracking is the gravitational pull of Jupiter so that the shell of ice is lifted up and let down again as it rotates round the planet causing some internal heating of the satellite. This heating up of Europa's interior by gravitational pull from Jupiter has a similarity to the heating up of the Earth's interior by the combined gravitational pull of the Sun and Moon.

Ganymede

Ganymede is Jupiter's largest moon but has a very low density. This means that, like Europa, it collected from the Jupiter/Planet X impact cloud sufficient ice particles to form a 100km thick shell of ice overlying a 900km deep ocean of water and ice slush. If Ganymede freed itself from Jupiter's gravity and collided with the bone dry planet Mercury then in an instant Mercury would be completely submerged in an ocean several hundred kilometres deep.

The most interesting feature of Ganymede is that it was itself a binary satellite consisting of two ice coated bodies, one darker in colour than the other, as a result of being formed in slightly different orbits round Jupiter. This binary subsequently collapsed leaving a supercontinent of dark coloured ice rock in a vast ocean of lighter water ice. This ice rock continent called Galileo Regio is, as expected, circular in shape and has a diameter of 4000km. It covers nearly a third of the hidden (from Jupiter) face of the satellite. Galileo Regio is a good illustration of how our own planet Earth once contained just one huge near circular supercontinent formed in a similar way, and it is pleasing to note that Ganymede's supercontinent of ice has not yet broken up into smaller continents as has happened with our own supercontinent.

Callisto

Callisto is smaller and less dense than Ganymede. Its surface is dark and is believed to be completely covered with a soil like material. However its density suggests that it has a very thick shell of ice, possibly more than 1000km thick. It seems probable that some time after it had developed this thick shell of ice it was involved in a major collision with a large asteroid. The force of the impact was sufficient to form a basin some 3000km in diameter and within this basin the shell has developed a series of concentric rings like waves formed when a stone is thrown into a pond. It is likely that the impact caused the asteroid to be completely vaporised and this material then formed a cloud of dust that enveloped the whole satellite. On cooling the dust settled on the satellite giving it the dark colour it has. Callisto therefore gives us a clue of how the Earth may have obtained some of its sediments and soil.

In conclusion to this chapter it may be said that Jupiter and its moons supports the theory that the Solar System was formed as a result of the collapse of a binary star, and the moons of Jupiter are interesting because they give us some insight into how the Solar System itself was formed and how the Earth was created.

Further Reading
Kaufmann W J *Discovering the Universe (Chapter 8)* W H Freeman & Co
New York 1990

APPENDIX EIGHT

SATURN, NEPTUNE, URANUS
AND PLUTO

'He also made the stars' (Gen. 1:16)

In this Appendix we take a brief look at the remaining planets to see if they also agree with the theory that we have proposed for their formation and also to see if they give us any clues about our own planet Earth.

Saturn

Saturn also began as a binary planet. Each of the iron cores of the semi-planets were formed in slightly different orbits in that part of the Planetary Disc where there was very little heavy dust but much of the ices made from the gases of various kinds.

These cores then began the task of gathering up the gases that surrounded them and in so doing both cores became heavier and moved further inwards in the Disc. A stage was reached when the two nearly complete semi planets came together at just the right velocity and a binary planet was formed and the two began to orbit round each other in the same way as our own Earth/Moon Binary.

While this went on both components of the binary were still in the process of sweeping up the remaining material from the Planetary Disc. A stage was reached when the two semi-planets became unbalanced and eventually collided with each other. The collapse of this binary system resulted, as expected, in the formation of a huge hot cloud of gas and dust.

The cloud behaved like all the other collision clouds that we have so far discussed. It began as an irregular shaped rotating cloud with many eddies, but the overall rotation preserved some of the original angular momentum of the binary system. The cloud then became roughly spherical, completely engulfing the now single planet. Eventually it flattened into a disc which then split up into rings.

View of Saturn

Fig. A8.1

Some of the outer rings of dust then aggregated to form belts of asteroids. These eventually were gathered together by small iron cores to form the ten moons of Saturn.

The inner rings however have still not aggregated into asteroid belts and are still observable from the Earth with modest telescopes. Some excellent photographs of these rings have been obtained by NASA space probes which in 1980/81 showed that the rings consisted of many hundreds of closely spaced thin bands of particles. When photographs of these rings were subjected to computer enhancement it was found that the banding of the rings were due to the different chemical composition of the particles in the ring.

This banding of the rings supports the theory which we have suggested for the sorting out of dust particles according to mass and chemical compositions. The same banding on a much larger scale also occurred when the Planetary Cloud formed a series of rings of dust around the dormant Sun and because of the banding of these rings we have planets of different compositions.

Thus in the ring system of Saturn we have a wonderful insight into what the Planetary Cloud might have looked like just after it had contracted and sorted itself out into rings, but before the rings then contracted into asteroid belts and planets.

The rings of Saturn have been given names for the purpose of further study. A closeup photograph of one of the rings (the F ring) showed that the bands had already begun to interfere with each other again so that this ring is now composed of five bands each about 10km in thickness intertwined to form braids, kinks and knots in this ring. This supports the theory that once the rings have been formed they continue to contract in size and in doing so concentrate the matter within them sufficiently to enable the formation of a belt of asteroids. The F ring is thus an illustration of the stage between a ring of dust and an asteroid belt.

Saturn has ten moons which in order outwards from the planet are Janus, Mimas, Enceladus, Tethys, Dione, Rhea, Titan,

Hyperion, Phoebe and Iapetus. These vary in size from little Phoebe which is only 40km in diameter to the giant Titan which at 5120km in diameter. All the moons lie well outside the ring system but the second nearest moon Mimas, which orbits Saturn every 22.6 hours, is only 112300 km from the outermost ring and is massive enough to be able to deplete the outermost ring of its particles on a regular basis. Mimas is therefore an illustration of how the core of a planet once formed is then able to pick up material from neighbouring rings and in doing so become even more powerful to continue the process until no more material is left. With each slight increase in mass Mimas will move closer to Saturn and its fate will be that it will either become too massive and crash land on Saturn or else it will devour all the rings and form a larger moon in a stable orbit around Saturn. The ten moons of Saturn should be regarded as the few that have survived as many more became too massive and were integrated back into the planet with little trace.

Titan has a density which as expected is very small considering that it was made from some of the lightest material in the cloud. It is believed that this moon is made of ices of water methane and ammonia with an atmosphere composed of mainly methane with some hydrogen and ethane. Titan gives us a clue as to how the Earth came to have huge reserves of gas and oil because if Titan has hydrocarbons without having life then the vast reserves of hydrocarbons that we have on the Earth today could be inorganic in origin and not organic as is currently believed.

Rhea, the next largest moon, is thought to be completely covered with water ice.

Iapetus has a diameter of 1600km and is interesting because it appears to be composed of two semimoons. One half of the moon is highly reflective of the Sun's light whereas the other half absorbs most of the light, suggesting different surface composition, which may be due to two different materials that have gone into the composition of this moon. Iapetus may thus be regarded as an example of a binary collapse in a relatively small body where the two parts simply coalesced without the usual cloud of dust being formed.

Hence in conclusion it may be said that Saturn increases our confidence about the theory of what happens after a binary collapse and gives us a wonderful illustration of how rings interact and how cores go about their business of gathering up material from rings. All this is very relevant to how the Earth was formed.

Uranus

Uranus also began its existence as two semi-planets which subsequently collided with each other to form a huge rotating cloud of gas and dust. In this case the collision was sufficiently violent to knock the single planet sideways so that its axis of rotation is inclined at 98 degrees to the plane of its orbit. This compares with the Earth's 23 degrees.

The cloud of gas formed in the collision behaved like all other similar clouds and now manifests itself into a system of five moons and at least eight narrow rings of particles.

Neptune

Neptune also began its existence as a binary planet. The collapse of this binary led to the formation of at least two moons and possibly several rings. Astronomers have deduced that Neptune has a source of internal heat. This is as expected because a collapse would result in the generation of a large amount of heat which appears to have not as yet dissipated.

Pluto/Charon Binary

Pluto is a binary system consisting of two semi-planets orbiting each other and only 19,700km apart. The main semi-planet called Pluto has a diameter of 2300km and was discovered in 1930. Its companion Charon has a diameter of 1280km but was detected nearly fifty years later. The Pluto-Charon binary is a very good example of the early stages of the formation of most of the rest of the planets including the Earth. It is possible that

Charon became a binary to Pluto less than 50 years ago and for this reason remained undetected for so long.

The Pluto-Charon binary is very young and it has not as yet settled into a stable orbit round the Sun. Its present orbit is highly elliptical so that its distance from the Sun is not constant but varies during its 248 year journey round it. At times the orbit of Pluto-Charon takes it inside Neptune's orbit and it is only a matter of time before the semi planets will be affected sufficiently for the balance to be upset and a collapse of the binary will then ensue.

Pluto has a density less than that of water which is as expected because the material from which the semi-planet was formed was obtained from the very low density particles at the outer reaches of the Solar Nebula Cloud and its size would not have allowed these particles to be tightly packed together. Observations suggest that the entire planet has a surface of frozen methane and an atmosphere rich in methane but also consisting of the very light gases like hydrogen and helium. These gases were present in abundance in this part of the Planetary Disc.

As far as can be ascertained there is nothing about the Pluto-Charon binary that is contrary to the theory for the formation of the Solar System that we have described.

In conclusion to this Appendix it may be said the formation and collapse of binary planets is the norm rather than a rare exception. This means that in the early history of the Solar System the number of smaller planets was much greater than today and to adequately explain our own planet Earth we need to explore the possibility that our planet also bears the hallmarks of being involved in a binary collapse and, this being the case, we can with reasonable justification apply what we have found out about other planets to our own planet Earth.

Further Reading
Kaufmann W J *Discovering the Universe (Chapter 8)* W H Freeman & Co New York 1990

APPENDIX NINE

LIFE ON EARTH

'he did not create it to be empty, but formed it to be inhabited' (Isaiah 45:18)

Evolution or Creation?

In the preceding chapters of this book the creation of the physical world - the soil, rock, air and water, was described but so far nothing has been said about the origin of the biosphere consisting of the plant, marine, bird and animal life of this planet.

While it is possible to give an explanation for how the Earth was formed according to the known laws of nature (apart from the initial conversion of energy into matter) there is, as yet, no scientific explanation for the origin of living organisms. Life cannot, it seems, be explained only in terms of the chemistry of organic molecules.

But the biosphere is the all important part of our planet and a book on the creation of the Earth is not complete without at least some attempt at an explanation of its origin.

Two common, but very different, beliefs currently exist and these may be described briefly as follows.

The Creation Belief

The vast majority of people of the world find it easier to believe in some version of the biblical truth which states that God in His infinite wisdom and power created life in all its variety, beauty and complexity in a supernatural way and that this was a very special, once only and wonderful miracle.

Hence according to this truth the explanation for the biosphere is quite simply that the *first* specimen or 'kind' of each form of life came into existence in a fully developed mature form, male and female, complete with seed or egg, in a matter of a few days, some six thousand years ago. Each of these life forms had a built in strong desire to procreate in the natural way, and thus all species multiplied rapidly to produce the biosphere much as we see it today.

The Theory of Evolution

This theory is believed by a small, but generally very influential, minority of people who find it difficult to accept the biblical truth on creation. The theory has being revised as a result of advances in molecular biology and genetics since it was first proposed by Darwin and Wallace over a hundred years ago. One fairly recent version of the theory suggested by a well known British naturalist runs as follows:

'About three billion years, ago while the Earth was still a hot planet, numerous volcanoes spewed out ash and lava into a thin oxygen free atmosphere of hydrogen, carbon monoxide, ammonia and methane. The Sun's ultraviolet rays were able to penetrate this atmosphere and at the same time the Earth was subject to violent electrical storms and in the ensuing lightning the mixture of gases in the atmosphere led to the formation of complex organic molecules including sugars, nucleic acids and amino acids. These molecules became so plentiful that they began to interact with each other and this went on for hundreds of millions of years until a very complex and long molecule of deoxyribonucleic acid (DNA for short) was formed.

DNA is different from other organic molecules in that it has an amazing ability to replicate itself and also to act as a set of instructions for the manufacture of amino acids.

In structure the DNA molecule is made up of two long strands of simpler molecules intertwined with each other.

At just the right moment the two strands are able to untwine themselves into two single strands, and each single strand then makes a copy of itself by manufacturing the right simpler molecules and placing them in the same right predetermined sequence and then intertwines with what it has made to form another double stranded complete DNA molecule and the whole process is then repeated.

Now the complex DNA molecule may be likened to a bacteria, so the earliest form of life was nothing more than bacteria.

Once bacteria was formed it became involved in a struggle for survival and was intelligent enough to realise that its chances of survival were better if it existed in colonies with other similar bacteria rather than on its own. So after a few hundred million years colonies of bacteria began to exist. All forms of life including Man may be regarded as immensely large colonies of bacteria. The evolution from inorganic matter to bacteria to man may be represented by the following chain or branches of transformations:

Hydrogen/Oxygen/Carbon - simple organic molecules - DNA - bacteria - photosynthesing bacteria - blue green algae - protozoa - sponge - jelly fish - coral - flatworm - brachipod - mollusc - bivalve - squid - worm - spider -crustacean - millipede - insect - fish - bird - mammal - ape -man.

The whole process started in the beginning of the Universe some fifteen billion years ago but DNA was formed about three billion years later and man did not develop until less than a million years ago.'

The theory of Evolution as outlined above is not compatible with the theory described in this book for the formation of the Earth because the former requires the Earth to be billions of years old whereas the latter says that life could not have begun on this planet until there was dry land and the Sun began to give heat and light and this was only about six thousand years ago.

The fossil record gives support to the biblical truth of creation and the theory for the Earth's formation described in this book. Contrary to popular opinion the fossil record does not support the assumption made in the theory of Evolution that life started with simple organisms which grew in complexity with the passage of time.

The choice between the biblical truth on Creation or the theory of Evolution is a matter of personal preference. It is not one that is made on scientific grounds because neither of these can be scientifically proved beyond reasonable doubt.

Life spirits

> *'creatures...when you take away their breath, they die and return to the dust...when you send your Spirit they are created.' {Ps.104:29}*

Science does not have a satisfactory explanation for the origin of life for two reasons.

Firstly if the biblical account that life began suddenly only a few thousand years ago is true, then there is simply no other explanation. Hence any attempt to try and find something that does not exist is bound to end in failure.

The second reason is that science has only considered half the problem. The physical part of every living organism is made out of atoms and molecules like everything else, but in addition to the physical part in living things there is an indwelling power and intelligence called its 'breath' or spirit.

It is this spirit which controls the physical part of the organism in every respect. It makes it grow and gives it desires and activates its defence mechanisms when attacked and heals it when it is injured.Death is a separation of the spirit part of life from its material part. This applies equally to the animal and vegetable kingdom.

This spirit has desires to grow in strength and stature but it can only do so by producing as many of its 'kind' as possible. Hence the very strong desire to procreate in every living organism.

Scientists have almost completely ignored the spirit in every living thing and for this reason have not been able to understand the origin of life.

The nearest evolutionists admit to the presence of a spirit is to call it 'Nature'.

While we would have little difficulty in accepting that a driving spirit or 'nature' is present in all life forms, the problem that has to be explained is the sudden appearance of millions of different species of life on this planet a mere six thousand years ago.

To solve this problem we need to split each life form into its two main constituents - the spirit part and the physical part- each has to be considered separately.

The biblical truth is that the physical part of each life form manifested itself suddenly only about six thousand years ago. But for this to have happened the spirit part had to exist before the first day.

This begs the question. Where did these 'life spirits' come from? We could answer this by saying that 'Nature' created the life spirits first. Nature is the physical manifestation of the Spirit of God and is endowed with all the power and intelligence it needs to create a particular life spirit.

It is God who creates a life spirit and this is done by thought alone since God has a Mind of infinite intelligence and an extremely powerful imagination. Thus a life spirit starts off as a mental conception. All the minute details of the proposed shape, size, colours and functions of the physical manifestation of the life spirit is then thought out. The 'life spirit' so created in the mind of God is then allowed to become a reality as a package of energy with instructions and intelligence. At this point Nature takes over and the life spirit now has to operate within the laws of nature. Thus it is only able to become a physical reality when the right environmental conditions exist.

It almost seems that the whole Earth was allowed to come

into existence for the sole purpose of providing the right environmental conditions for the myriads of life spirits to become physical realities.

The life spirit, being spirit, is able to travel the length and width of a galaxy in search of just the right conditions it needs to make a physical manifestation of itself. It is not surprising therefore that the newly completed Earth attracted so many life spirits so quickly.

To make a physical manifestation of itself all a life spirit has to do is to follow its own in built instructions to gather together of the necessary materials and assemble these according to plan. For a life spirit to become a physical reality is not always possible because the life spirit has to operate within the laws of nature for the behaviour of physical matter. It is for this reason that living things appear to have 'evolved' from inanimate matter.

The physical part of all living things are composed of organic molecules. These molecules are made from the atoms of only a few elements all of which are made from electrons, neutrons and protons which are really quantities of energy.Hence all molecules may be regarded as bundles of energy.

This being the case we should think of the physical part of living things as an extremely intricate interlocking between untold trillions of bundles of energy.

A life spirit has been powered to control the inferior energy of matter so armed with detailed instructions the life spirit can assemble matter as required. In this way molecules of exactly the right sort are made to come together strictly as programmed. Hence to fully understand a life form we need to understand **both** the physical part made up of organic molecules as well as the life spirit of that form.

Biologists have tended to look closely only at the physical part of living things- the cells with its coded DNA and so on- and have not paid too much attention to its life spirit except to call it Nature.

From Life spirit to DNA

The transformation from a life spirit to the *first* physical specimen of its kind can now be explained.

Life spirits were willed into existence in a highly charged state ready and willing to become physical realities as soon as they found the right conditions.

All living things start as a single cell and develop and grow by a controlled doubling of its cells.

Hence if we can understand how the first cell of each kind of living form was formed the rest is not too difficult to follow as it can be readily observed in nature.

It has long been suggested that life may have originated in space rather than on the Earth. Many scientist believe that life was introduced to this planet by comets. This theory may at first sight seem to be in disagreement with the Genesis account of how life started on the Earth but this is not necessarily so.

As explained above life spirits had in built coded instructions and energy to construct their first cell from matter that had already been formed.

The first opportunity that a life spirit had to gather the right sort of elements and simple molecules required to make its first cell was well before the first day. All the necessary elements and molecules were certainly available in the rings of gas and dust of the Planetary Disc long before the planets were formed.

All of the elements needed to make the first cell of every 'kind' of life were available in a free state. A constant stream of protons and electrons from the Solar Wind also ensured the availability and mobility of the ingredients required for cell making.

The life spirit of each 'kind' was able to start the process of constructing its physical form using the simple organic molecules that were formed in the Planetary Disc. In the rings of this disc, gases such as water vapour, methane and ammonia were plentiful. To assemble these tiny bits of matter all that was required was a set of clear instructions and energy which each life spirit had. Hence the first simple molecules for life were probably assembled in space as many scientists now think.

The simple molecules so formed were then charged by the energy of the life spirit to combine with other simple molecules to form much more complex organic molecules.

These complex molecules were then arranged, again according to instructions, into the intended DNA molecule. Once completed the DNA molecule so formed was charged to attract other molecules around it to form a protective wall.

Once each 'kind' of life spirit assembled its first cell it was able to preserve in the DNA molecule it had so formed the complete set of precious instructions it been entrusted with and so encoded its DNA in the manner we find today.

A DNA molecule made by a life spirit is capable of storing enormous amounts of information. It is now believed that the next generation of computers will not use silicon chips but DNA and a leading expert in this field recently stated that there is more information storage capacity in a milligram of DNA than there is in a combination of all the of the computers in the world today!

In the fullness of time life spirits of thousands of different 'kinds' [Gen.1:20] of life could have found all they needed to form their first cells in the Planetary Disc.

Once formed, the cells may have remained inactive as minute but very precious specks of dust for just the right conditions to prevail in order for them to be able to bloom into physical creatures.

Once the Earth was completed some of these very precious life containing specks landed on it. Some would have remained in the atmosphere, some would have found their way into the oceans and some would have settled on dry land.

Some probably still lie deeply embedded in rocks and soils and ocean and lake beds.

It is possible that other specks or spores of life landed on other planets where they may still be there waiting in vain for the right conditions for them to blossom into living things.

When conditions on the Earth became ideal these highly energised cells sprung into action almost instantaneously.

Life as we know it began quite suddenly as the fossil records suggest and as described in the Book of Genesis.

The scenario given above for the formation of the cell and DNA is very different from the one suggested by evolutionists which involves a different atmosphere on our planet, lightening storms and accidents in primeval soups. Our scenario suggests that the rings of gases and dust in the early Solar System were ideal for the formation of DNA and its enclosing cell wall but only through an input of instructions trusted to its life spirit.

For this reason meteorites found on Earth today sometimes contain microfossils and such microfossils are likely to be found on other planets as well. The usual explanation for microfossils in meteorites found on the Earth is that they are of terrestrial origin and this of course could also be the case.

The seeds of life in the form of microscopic grains of dust were probably sown all over the supercontinent and in the global ocean and atmosphere for some time before the Sun burst into heat and light quite suddenly.

The first rays of sunshine were all that was required to stir the dormant cells into action. When activated by light, moisture, oxygen and an abundance of raw material of the right kind, the highly energised seeds of life were able to burst into activity. From a single cell two were formed and from these two four were formed and so on. Multiplication of the cells would have been extremely rapid in the ideal conditions of the warm and humid Earth about six thousand years ago.

The cells would have doubled in number every few minutes guided by the intelligence in its DNA molecule so that in a short space of time sufficient cells to make the first fully grown specimen of tree, animal, fish, bird and animal would have formed. If doubling of the cells took place every say three minutes then enough cells to form a complete fully grown creature would have been formed in only a few hours and the first cell of each life form was intentionally highly charged to behave in this way.

The first form of life to appear was *'seed-bearing plants and trees on the land..'*

> *'The land produced vegetation,'* {Gen.1:12}

The next form life spirit to manifest itself was in the seas

> *'Let the water teem with living creatures'* {Gen.1:20}

followed quickly by the appearance of bird and animal life

> *' ... had formed out of the ground all the beasts of the field and the birds of the air'* {Gen.2:19}

The first man became a physical reality only a few days after the plants and animals were created. He too began as a cell in the dust of the ground

> *'...formed the man from the dust of the ground..'* {Gen.2:7}

All the first specimens of life had in built seeds and eggs and a strong desire to multiply - a desire that has remained undiminished to this day.

Reproductions of the first specimens manifested themselves over the entire supercontinent. The same happened in the global oceans at a rate much faster than the present one because of the original virility and strength of the life spirit of the 'kind'. In this way in a matter of only a few years the Earth gained its very rich and healthy biosphere.

Today life spirits in living organisms are easily observed at work in all plant and animal life. These life spirits are copies of the original with some modifications to cater for local environmental conditions because life spirits have been instructed to multiply but can only do so by natural sexual reproduction. For this reason the sex drive in all living forms remains very powerful even today.

In a tree that is living the life spirit controls each cell of the tree and allows and directs the formation of new cells so that the tree grows and produces branches, leaves and fruit. But when the tree dies there is no life spirit and the cells in the tree cease to multiply or replace themselves and the tree becomes lifeless matter which will rot and eventually become dust again. There is no chemical difference in a living creature just before and just after its death because death simply implies an absence of its non material life spirit.

Thus it is incorrect to look at a living thing as just a mere collection of organic molecules as some scientists do. We also need to study the life spirit of the organism and to do this we have to be prepared to accept that a super intelligence and power called God is alone able to form life spirits. All forms of life may be looked upon as physical manifestations of their life spirits.

Thus all life forms including every plant, fish, bird and animal that we see on the Earth began not by an accident of nature in a mythical soup with magical electrical storms and imaginary fights for survival, but as a deliberate act of will power and intelligence of the Universal Spirit of God.

Man is also a very special life spirit and still carries that spirit within him and we have more to say on this later on.

The theory of Evolution assumes the existence of a life spirit but the word 'spirit' is strictly unacceptable. Instead the word 'nature' is used frequently for the same thing. Evolutionists also do not seem to like the idea of giving nature infinite wisdom and are more comfortable with the idea that nature must lack intelligence and therefore has to go through a learning process and so the concept of billions of years and accidental evolution has been introduced.

It is not 'evolution' but the intelligent life spirit within every life form that knows how and when to make changes in its physical manifestation to suit environmental conditions. The life spirit in a living organism does not have either the power or intention of changing its physical manifestation altogether. Apes cannot become humans and dogs cannot become horses but variations within apes, humans, dogs and horses are of course possible because the intelligent life spirit in each of these life forms is bound on one hand to keep to the original design but has the ability to make slight modifications to the design to suit local conditions- a feature evolutionists call natural selection and adaptation.

Without the life spirit in every living form there would be have been no life on this planet. But if this life spirit is considered the explanation for life on this planet becomes logical but still leaves us in great awe of the magnificence, power and intelligence of the Spirit of God or as atheists would prefer the Spirit of Nature.

Today as we gaze in admiration at the form of an animal, bird, fish or tree and are struck by its divine beauty and marvellous construction, we have to remind ourselves that all these are authentic reproductions of an original which began as a thought in the Mind of the Spirit of God.

The life spirit in all living things is multiplied with little loss of power and passed on in the normal natural methods of procreation and sexual reproduction so that the life spirit lives on in greater strength in each generation of its species. It is able to make minor modifications as required to survive comfortably for as long as possible. When however conditions become unacceptable the species cannot survive any longer and becomes extinct. When this happens the life spirit becomes incapable of further physical manifestation and fades away into oblivion. Millions of different 'kinds' of life spirits have perished in this way so all we see on the Earth today are the millions more that have survived.

The life spirit of every life form is a very precious thing. For this reason, before the Great Flood, steps had to be taken to safeguard the surviving animals and birds to prevent them from becoming extinct. And Noah had to spend over a century of his life in building a vessel just to preserve the species that then existed.

Man on Earth

According to the theory of Evolution man descended from apes who once swung from trees in the jungles of Africa. The theory for the final stages in the evolution of man postulates that as the climate of the Earth changed and rainfall decreased the jungles shrunk and allowed open grasslands to develop. The apes were thus forced out of the jungle and had to forage for food in the tall grass and this meant that the apes had to adopt an upright position to see over the grass. As they did so the theory goes on they began to lose their hair in order to stay cool in the blazing sun of the open Savannah and so after about a million years the hairless upright ape we call man evolved. The large brain of man is thought to have developed by accident!

While creationists would dismiss the above scenario as plain nonsense there are many evolutionist scientists who would be prepared to defend the thesis that this was the path taken in the transformation from ape to man.

But if we accept that God is highly intelligent and that has bestowed some of this intelligence to the human life spirit then the story of man's emergence on this planet is very different and is as follows.

Some six thousand years ago God designed and released the life spirit of the first human. This very special life spirit built up its first cell which became embedded in the dust of this planet. When conditions for human life became absolutely ideal the cell multiplied rapidly and after only a few hours the first fully grown human specimen called Adam came into existence.

271

'And the Lord God formed man from the dust of the ground...'
(Gen.2:7)

God intended that this man would live for ever-the controlling spirit in him was made powerful enough for that purpose. Hence a cell taken from him was easily altered to produce another human being in the form of the first female.

From these two people natural reproduction by normal sexual means was able to take place and from this couple the entire population of the world has emerged. The great diversity of skin colour, hair and facial features in the human population today is testimony to the power of the original human spirit to adapt and change to suit local conditions.

If the human population of the world doubled every fifty years then a simple calculation will show that the present population of the Earth of some 6000 million people could be easily attained in much less than six thousand years from just this one couple. Every single person who now lives on this planet is a manifestation of the original human spirit which can be traced right back to the Mind of God.

The great explosion in the human population of the world today is thus a testimony of the power of the first human spirit.

Further Reading
Attenborough D *Life on Earth* William Collins and BBC Books London 1995
Watson Lyall *Lifetide* Book Club Associates London 1979

APPENDIX TEN

THE AGE OF THE EARTH

'Altogether Adam lived 930 years, and then he died' (Gen.5:5)

4500 million years old?

We in the western world are constantly reminded in scientific journals and by the media that the Earth is at least 4500 million years old and that all the Earth's physical and biological features can be adequately explained by slow evolutionary processes over this vast period of time. We read about dinosaurs that became extinct suddenly about 65 million years ago or about the first appearance of living forms some 500 million years ago and about the evolution of man from apes about a million years ago and so on. From our early schooldays we have been conditioned to believe that the Earth is so old that all the traces of its beginning have long been eradicated and that the events of the beginnings do not matter any more, being so far back in time.

This view of the world is very unfortunate because it has made us think only about the survival and comfort of our physical selves - our flesh, bones and blood which are only temporary parts of our true selves. We have lost almost all interest in the well being of the life spirit which we carry and which will survive our physical death and which is part of the Spirit of God.

Because man has lost sight of his true origin and does not know or care about the final destiny of his life spirit the human condition and this once very beautiful planet of ours is now in a mess. Man is not in harmony with Nature or with his fellow inhabitants on this planet.

The attitude that many people seem to have is that the Earth has survived for 4500 million years and that it will do so for at least a few hundred million years more so our mere three score and ten years on this planet seems hardly capable of making any impression on it.

But if the story of the Earth's creation and the creation of life as related in this book is correct then our perspective on our planet and ourselves ought to be quite different.

We may be more inclined to be concerned with the preciousness of the eternal life spirit within us and take steps to ensure its survival and comfort in its next manifestation - and there will be another one for every person who has ever lived on this planet, however good or evil his first life has been.

But by believing that the Earth is 4500 million years old and that all forms of life including our own is merely the result of a series of accidents involving the vagaries of the behaviour of molecules, and that there is no such thing as an intelligent life spirit within us, we cut ourselves off from the Spirit of God that allowed us to become intelligent beings with free will. Free to attempt to go it alone and free to come under His control and care.

To know the age of the earth we really need to know when it was created, but as we have seen the Earth did not begin to exist from a particular day like a new born baby.

The Earth began as a small ball of iron and then grew steadily layer by layer from then on. If we say that the first tiny ball of iron increased in diameter by just one millimetre every thirty years then the Earth would have taken about 4500 million years to grow into its present size.

However we are not really concerned about how long it took for the Earth to reach its present size because what matters to us most is not the age of the whole Earth but the date in history when the supercontinent emerged from below the waves of the sea. Archbishop Ussher of Ireland worked this out in 1664 and declared that the supercontinent became dry land in 4004 BC.

This is an estimate based on ages of important people given in the Bible and there is no scientific evidence to suggest that this estimate is incorrect.

A little thought suggests that the figure of 6000 years makes a lot more sense than the 200+ million years assumed by some Earth Scientists for the time when the supercontinent broke up.

For example, much of the land mass on the Earth in the last century was in an untouched virgin condition and everywhere there were signs of youthful freshness.

It does seem a little odd that the Americas were only discovered a few hundred years ago and vast tracts of prime land on these mighty continents were very sparsely populated until only a few decades ago.

The 4.5 billion year estimate for the Earth's age became acceptable only to those who wanted to cling to the idea that life began and developed on this planet very slowly by evolution without the help of the Spirit of God.

The 4500 million year estimate is based largely on scant information and wild assumptions about meteorites.

Many meteorites have been recovered from the Earth's surface and their age determined by what is called radiometric methods. In this method the analyst looks for certain elements called parent radioactive isotopes such as Carbon 14, Rubidium 87, Uranium 235, Uranium 238, or Thorium 232. These decay into daughter isotopes Nitrogen 14, Strontium 87, Lead 207, Lead 206, and Argon 40 respectively. The rates of decay for each of these can be accurately determined so the reasoning is that if the amount of parent and daughter in a meteorite can be measured accurately then the age of the meteorite can be determined.

This seems logical enough but on closer examination there are very serious difficulties. Firstly the method assumes that to begin with only the parent isotope was present in the meteorite and that there was no loss of either parent or daughter during its life. A little thought shows that there can be no justification for this assumption because meteorites were formed in one of the rings in the Planetary Disc and in these rings elements were sorted out by the cosmic wind and other forces according to atomic masses, and radioactive elements were no exception to this rule. As there is very little difference between the atomic masses of parent and daughter we could normally expect a meteorite to have had good amounts of both daughter and parent from the very beginning and this has proved to be the case so the actual proportion of each tells us nothing.

For this study iron meteorites were chosen because it was thought that these meteorites were the remains of the inner cores of planets that fragmented for some reason! Hence even if the age was correct what is being estimated is not the age of the Earth but the radiometric age (not the real age) of the meteorite, and this has no relevance to the time when the Earth acquired its supercontinent of dry land.

Meteorites also heat up as they enter the Earth's atmosphere and again on impact. All this will have an effect on the amount of radioactive isotopes. Despite these very significant problems the average age of the meteorites as determined by this method is taken as about 4500 million years, and this figure has mistakenly been adopted as the age of the Earth. This is as illogical as determining the age of a house by the age of a stone thrown through a window or by one of its bricks. If we knew for certain how and when the bricks were manufactured and if we could be sure that they were used immediately after they were manufactured, then the age of the brick and the house would be about the same. But if the bricks were left in a yard to mature for a few decades or reused after demolition of an earlier building then we might still be able to determine the age of the brick (by the date stamp) but this would not be the age of the house. As the Earth was made from mature asteroids and meteors it is not logical to use their age (even if this could be determined accurately) to date the age of the Earth, because we do not know for sure how long these meteorites were maturing in space before being used to build the Earth.

Geologists have also attempted to estimate the age of some sedimentary rocks by the rate at which sediments carried by water form into layers when allowed to settle. By adding together the time for many such layers to form the total time required can, they say, be determined and from this an estimate of the age of a particular layer can be determined.

The problem with this method is that almost 99% of the vast amount of sediments on the Earth today were not formed by slow erosion of hard rocks by wind and water and glaciers but arrived on this planet in a single day wrapped up in the basaltic shell of baby planet Pangaea. For this reason the total volume of sediments on the Earth is truly vast and probably exceeds the volume of the water in the oceans.

The ocean floors, particularly near the land masses have layers of sediment thousands of metres thick. This is as expected because the crashed planetesimal was subject to gigantic tidal waves which would have the effect of spreading out the contained sediments.

During the numerous oscillations of the basaltic shell after the Earth captured the Moon, some of the sediments which had accumulated on the ocean floor were suddenly transported in huge quantities and deposited in thick layers over vast areas of land and sea in a matter of hours or days, or at most months.

Hence the assumption of slow rates of erosion and deposition is valid for short periods of comparative peace but any estimation of the age of the Earth based on sediment build up rates must be regarded as totally incorrect. A modern geological map would show less than 0.5% of the land containing what is called recent alluvium, which is material that has been eroded and transported by rivers or streams or glaciers.

The type of fossil contained in a rock specimen is also used to ascribe an age to the rock. This is based on the assumption that the age of the fossil is known. This is an erroneous assumption because the age of a fossil is based on the supposed age of the strata in which it is found and the age of the strata is incorrect in the first place.

Fossils are generally formed in catastrophic conditions. Millions of animals die on the Earth each day but they do not form fossils unless they are buried immediately after death or death was due to instant burial, as seems to be the case for most fossils.

Hence the existence of a good record of fossils simply testifies to the many catastrophes involving the sudden transportation of huge quantities of preformed sediments into areas teeming with life. As the basaltic shell was subject to numerous upheavals after life had begun on the Earth it is interesting to note that each upheaval has fossilised somewhat different life forms in each cycle, presumably because of changing temperature conditions.

The fossils also start appearing very suddenly. Both these facts are in agreement with the life spirit theory for the formation of the biosphere, because life on this planet only began in earnest when conditions were right, but numerous writhings of the sediment laden ocean floor caused widespread death which put a check on the very rapid rate of growth and multiplication of all life forms including man. It is worth mentioning that animals which were highly mobile formed less fossils than those that could not move away quickly and this is reflected in the fossil record.

The young Earth

'.. speak to the earth, and it will teach you.' (Job 12:8)

It is very strange that the incorrect and complicated methods which give the age of the Earth in billions of years have gained so much acceptance when there are simpler methods which indicate a much younger planet.

Some of the simpler methods for estimating when life began on this planet may be briefly mentioned here.

Crumbling mountains and receding coastlines

High mountains were formed when large land masses floated away as explained earlier and then came to a sudden halt when an obstruction was met. For example the Himalayan range of mountains formed suddenly when India moved from its place near southern Africa and crashed into the continent of Asia. With every mountain range there is an associated obstruction. The land involved in the collisions was mainly weak sedimentary rocks often containing fossils and for this reason many mountains are also made from sedimentary rocks. These mountains are now crumbling back to their sediments at an alarming rate. The Bay of Bengal is rapidly being silted up as a result of the silt and sand washed down from the Himalayan mountains by several rivers. The scree at the base of many mountains testify how natural weathering is also able to chip away whole mountain sides.

Coastlines where the land is made from sediments also recede at an alarming rate by the relentless action of the sea. If these rates of erosion continue a simple calculation would show that the sediments that make up the mountains and land masses should end up as jumbled up mass of sediments on the sea floor in less than a million years. Hence the notion that the continents are hundreds of millions of years old is not scientific as these continents should have by now long disappeared to the sea floor never to emerge again.

Asteroid population

There are a very large number of asteroids and comets still in the Solar System. This suggests that the process of accretion has not yet been completed, and from this we can assume that the Solar System cannot be very old. A few million years is sufficient for the Sun to reclaim all the material now in orbit around it and spiralling towards it but as this has not as yet happened the conclusion must be that not sufficient time has elapsed since the collapse of the Binary Sun.

The Earth's Magnetic field

The Earth's magnetic field decreases in intensity by 50% every 1400 years. This means that only about 20,000 years ago the intensity would have been far too great for comfort and life would have been impossible.

It is reasonable to accept that life began on this planet when the intensity of the magnetic field reached a tolerable level and this would be a few thousand and not a few million years ago.

The salt in the sea

The salinity of the oceans has also been used to estimate the age of the Earth. The argument here is that salts are washed down by rivers and ground water from the continental land masses and accumulate in the oceans and therefore if we can measure the amount of salt in the oceans, we should be able to tell how long this process has been going for. Scientists who have done this have been a little surprised to find that the amount of salt in the sea is not as great as it should be. This is not unexpected.

According to the theory that has been described in this book the waters of the world oceans were once trapped below the basaltic shell and when these waters broke out it already had salts of all kinds already dissolved in it. The supercontinent was immersed in this ocean and any salt that was contained in the planetesimal Pangaea would have been partly dissolved by the waters of the ocean. When the supercontinent emerged from below the sea a great deal of water evaporated, leaving quantities of salt still on the land. Today rain water is still dissolving these salts and it is for this reason our rivers contain a high proportion of salt. The fact that the sea is not as salty as it should be if the Earth is millions of years old simply means that the process of fresh water washing away the salts from the land has only been going on for a few thousand years and not for millions of years.

Human Population

At present the world's population doubles every 42 years. This is an annual growth rate of 1.7%. Had this been the rate of population growth from the time of Adam and Eve then it would have taken only 1300 years for the world's population to have grown to its present level of 6000 million.

If we assume a much lower annual growth rate of only 0.2% and started with just one couple 100,000 years ago the population of the world today would have been estimated as hundreds of millions of times greater than what it actually is.

Such simplistic estimates of the predicted population from the current growth rate are of course not valid. Climatic changes, famines, epidemics and wars will take their toll and make a great difference to any estimate.

The Bible tells us that the entire population of the world apart from four couples were exterminated in the Great Flood which was only 4400 years ago. So starting from these four couples and using a very modest growth rate of 0.5% the world would have attained a population of 1600 million by the end of the nineteenth century.

All these figures do not help us to estimate the age of the Earth but clearly if the first couple were on the Earth a few million years ago then somewhere on this planet we should find the remains of civilisations that had destroyed themselves by over population and so far no such evidence has been found.

The biblical truth is that man arrived on this planet a mere six thousand years ago and was almost entirely wiped out in about 2400 B.C. Man is only expected to continue living on this planet for another thousand years. This is all the time that God has allowed for man to unite his life spirit with His own and thus be allowed to live forever as a worthy and eternal member of the Universe.

Further Reading
Hurley P M *How Old is the Earth?* Doubleday and Company New York 1959
Press F & Siever R *Earth* (Second Edition) W H Freeman & Co San Francisco 1977